SAVE HARMLESS AGREEMENT

Because use of the information, instructions and materials discussed and shown in this book, document, electronic publication or other form of media is beyond our control, the purchaser or user agrees, without reservation to save Knowledge Publications Corporation, its agents, distributors, resellers, consultants, promoters, advisers or employees harmless from any and all claims, demands, actions, debts, liabilities, judgments, costs and attorney's fees arising out of, claimed on account of, or in any manner predicated upon loss of or damage to property, and injuries to or the death of any and all persons whatsoever, occurring in connection with or in any way incidental to or arising out of the purchase, sale, viewing, transfer of information and/or use of any and all property or information or in any manner caused or contributed to by the purchaser or the user or the viewer, their agents, servants, pets or employees, while in, upon, or about the sale or viewing or transfer of knowledge or use site on which the property is sold, offered for sale, or where the property or materials are used or viewed, discussed, communicated, or while going to or departing from such areas.

Laboratory work, scientific experiment, working with hydrogen, high temperatures, combustion gases as well as general chemistry with acids, bases and reactions and/or pressure vessels can be EXTREMELY DANGEROUS to use and possess or to be in the general vicinity of. To experiment with such methods and materials should be done ONLY by qualified and knowledgeable persons well versed and equipped to fabricate, handle, use and or store such materials. Inexperienced persons should first enlist the help of an experienced chemist, scientist or engineer before any activity thereof with such chemicals, methods and knowledge discussed in this media and other material distributed by KnowledgePublications Corporation or its agents. Be sure you know the laws, regulations and codes, local, county, state and federal, regarding the experimentation, construction and or use and storage of any equipment and or chemicals BEFORE you start. Safety must be practiced at all times. Users accept full responsibility and any and all liabilities associated in any way with the purchase and or use and viewing and communications of knowledge, information, methods and materials in this media.

FUEL CELLS

Power for Tomorrow

www.KnowledgePublications.com

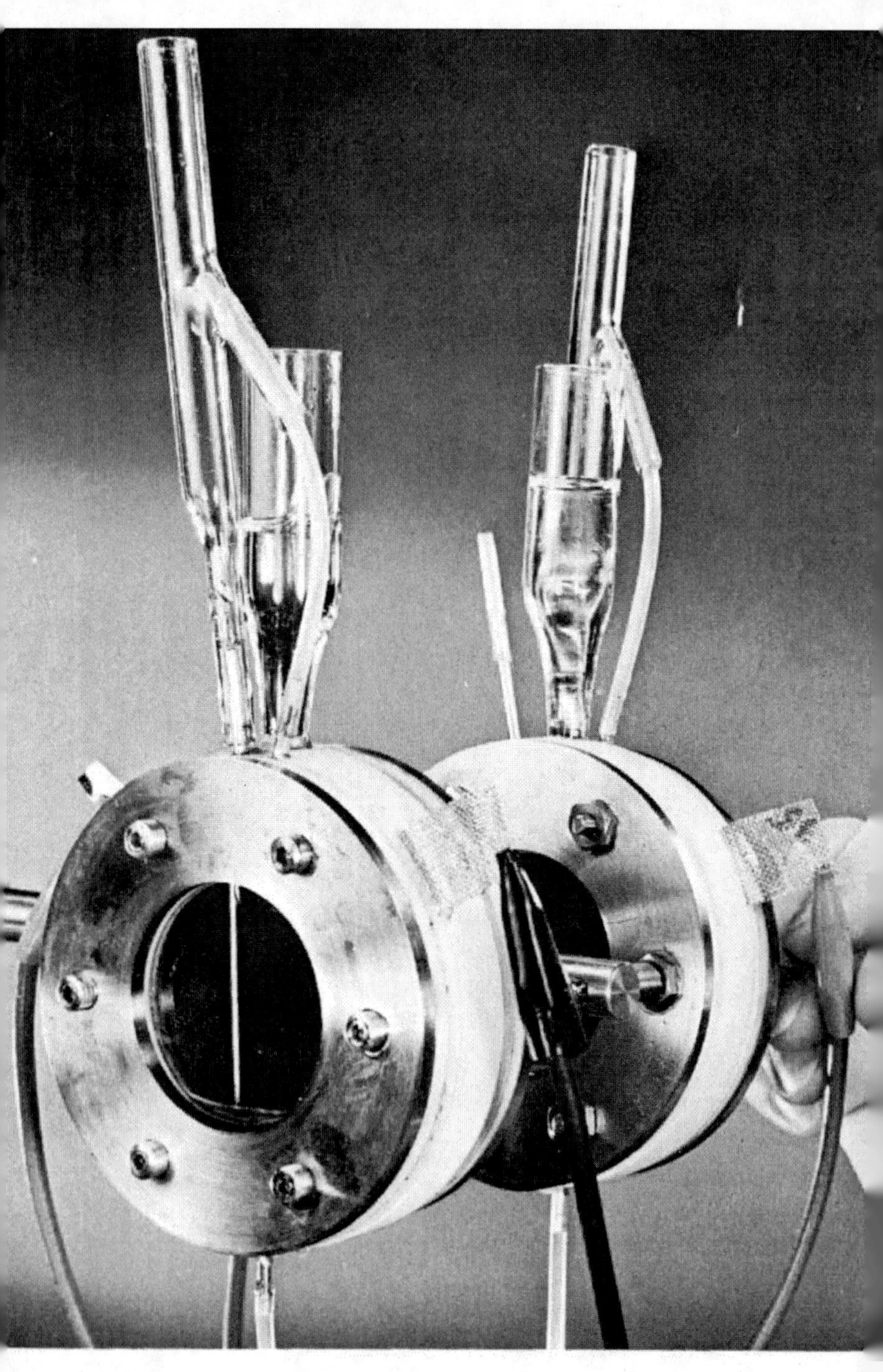

Producing electricity by chemical reaction, two fuel cells linked in series provide voltage to run a motor. Octane is the fuel; by-products are harmless carbon dioxide and pure water.

D. S. Halacy, Jr.

FUEL CELLS

Power for Tomorrow

with drawings by Frank Aloise

THE WORLD PUBLISHING COMPANY

CLEVELAND AND NEW YORK

Grateful acknowledgment is made to the following for providing photographs for reproduction in this book: Allis-Chalmers Manufacturing Company, page 16; Esso Research and Engineering Company, pages 68, 137, 138, 140, 141; General Dynamics, page 12; General Electric Research Laboratory, frontispiece, pages 10, 76, 104, 107; *Harper's Magazine* (1896), pages 31, 32, 34; *Life* Magazine, © 1962 Time Inc. (all rights reserved), pages 92, 93; *Philosophical Magazine* (1842), page 24; *Popular Electronics*, pages 95, 97; Pratt and Whitney Aircraft, pages 18, 37, 59, 62, 102; Union Carbide Corporation, page 20; U. S. Army, pages 118, 125.

Published by The World Publishing Company
2231 West 110th Street, Cleveland 2, Ohio
Published simultaneously in Canada by
Nelson, Foster & Scott Ltd.
Library of Congress Catalog Card Number: 66-13907
ISBN:978-1-60322-018-7

Designed by Jack Jaget

www.KnowledgePublications.com

Contents

FUEL CELLS

Power for Tomorrow

www.KnowledgePublications.com

CHAPTER ONE

Space-age Power Plant

IN THE SHORT span of time since World War II, a new kind of engine has progressed from a mere laboratory curiosity to a practical power source that may revolutionize the world of machines. It is called the fuel cell. We live in the space age, and it was space flight that first gave the new power plant an opportunity to prove itself. The manned spacecraft Gemini with their remarkable flights have dramatically introduced the fuel cell to the world and caused the comment that here was a development potentially as revolutionary as that of atomic energy.

To select the Gemini power supply, NASA experts considered many different methods of producing electricity in space. Nuclear plants may one day do the job, but they are not ready yet. Internal combustion engines such as are used in cars would pose problems of noxious exhaust gases, heat removal, and reliability of operation. Storage batteries seemed to be the solution, as they have been on Mercury space capsules and other vehicles, but they proved to be too heavy.

The special nickel-cadmium storage batteries used in Mer-

Two General Electric fuel-cell batteries (cylindrical containers) are shown in a Gemini spacecraft.

cury did an excellent job, but power for orbital flight could require batteries weighing as much as the astronaut. And for longer missions storage batteries might weigh more than a ton! As big a weight penalty as that presented an enormous problem. The revolutionary fuel cell, literally a "battery with a gas tank," provided the solution.

Late in 1963 a small, "pilot model" fuel cell with an output of 50 watts was launched into space. The pioneer power supply passed its test with flying colors, withstanding the low temperature, vacuum, radiation, and zero gravity of outer space. NASA planners breathed a long sigh of relief, for nearing completion were big, two-kilowatt fuel cells for the two-man Gemini spacecraft and the larger Apollo. The Gemini fuel cell weighs about 500 pounds complete and can furnish power ranging from 500 to 2,000 watts for as long as fifteen days. Fueled with hydrogen and oxygen, the cell is silent in operation and has no moving parts.

When our Apollo moon flight vehicle goes into space, it too will carry a fuel cell that will produce about the same power as the Gemini fuel cell. Also being developed is a smaller fuel cell for the Apollo's LEM, or Lunar Excursion Module, which will land the astronauts on the moon. These space power plants cost many millions of dollars to develop; they must offer tremendous advantages to justify this great cost.

As it has for many other devices, space exploration has been a boost for the fuel cell. On the strength of advances made since space designers first eyed it eagerly, the new power plant is being hailed by some as one to make the internal-combustion engine and the steam engine as obsolete as dodo birds. Following completion of the Gemini 5 flight, a

Star I *submarine is powered by an Allis-Chalmers 750-watt hydrazine-oxygen fuel-cell system.*

spokesman for General Electric, the firm which built the fuel cells used in the eight-day mission, predicted early application of the new device in many fields. Fuel cells, he said, would be installed aboard submarines for use in "inner space" as well as outer space. The military would use them to power vehicles; industry would make similar use, as well as adapt them for portable communications equipment including remote TV cameras.

Consumer use of fuel cells was foreseen in such a variety of chores as powering electric blankets, house trailers, lawn mowers, and even as emergency power for the whole house when necessary. Such small fuel cells were thought to be possible within two years. On a longer timetable, fuel-cell power for automobiles was suggested as a logical development.

Most of our power today is produced by heat engines, whose efficiency is governed by a law of thermodynamics discovered by French scientist Sadi Carnot more than a century ago. A "Carnot-cycle" engine does not use all the heat supplied to it and thus cannot be even theoretically 100 per cent efficient. Very efficient gasoline engines and other internal-combustion engines deliver only about 25 to 30 per cent efficiency. Even the best steam-turbine electric generators cannot better a figure of about 40 per cent. More than half the fuel in a heat engine is therefore wasted, and there seems no hope of materially increasing its efficiency.

The present degree of efficiency of heat engines is the result of many years of intense effort in that direction. But the fuel cell, demonstrated as a practical power source only since World War II, already delivers from 50 to 75 per cent efficiency! And in theory it can approach a full 100 per cent. Not a heat engine, the fuel cell is a direct converter of chemical energy to electrical energy that promises to deliver more power per pound of fuel than anything else except a nuclear power plant.

There is another important advantage besides that of efficiency. Large turboelectric plants are complicated high-speed engines, expensive to build and to maintain. They are built of precisely fitting, rapidly moving parts and are subject to wear and mechanical failure. They also require many steps in converting fuel into electricity. First a coal or oil or gas fire heats water to make steam. Then the steam drives a turbine, and finally the turbine operates a generator to produce electricity. But the fuel cell has *no* moving parts—unless we count the electrons that form the electric current. It bypasses all the conventional engine's intermediate steps and quietly converts fuel to electricity in a single step.

Conventional power plants are noisy, they can blow up or catch fire, and they sometimes produce harmful exhaust gases. Although fuel cells do produce by-products, these are not only harmless but often useful as well, like the water produced by the Apollo and Gemini cells. A submarine fuel cell produces salt, and another being considered for long space flights may furnish not only water but food for the men aboard—all in addition to electric power. The alarming power failure in November 1965, which plunged much of the Northeast into darkness and halted all operations depending on electric power, pointed out a danger in depending on a single, gigantic power supply. Because the fuel cell does not have to be of huge size to be efficient, it may conceivably lead to smaller, local power plants for domestic and industrial electricity.

Since the fuel cell is apparently such a wonderful power plant, we might well ask why we have spent so much time and money on heat engines that waste more than half the fuel they burn, particularly since the fuel cell was first suggested more than one hundred and fifty years ago, and working models were built soon after that. Unfortunately, the device was far ahead of its time, somewhat like Hero's steam engine and Da Vinci's airplane and parachute.

Men have known about electricity for some two thousand years. Early Romans even used electric fish in shock treatments for the mentally ill. It was an argument between Italian scientists Galvani and Volta about animal electricity that led the latter to discover the "voltaic pile" or electrochemical battery at the beginning of the nineteenth century. In this first artificial battery, dissimilar materials were placed together to cause a flow of electrons through a wire connected to them.

The early electric battery was a marvelously simple device for converting fuel to power, but it was soon suggested that the battery might be improved by supplying fuel rather than letting the battery consume itself. By 1839 Sir William Grove did just that, making a battery to which hydrogen and oxygen could be added from outside.

In 1889 other men produced an improvement on Grove's device and dubbed it a "fuel cell." But by then the dynamo, an electromagnetic device that converted mechanical movement into electricity, was coming into popularity. A steam engine could be connected to a dynamo and produce large amounts of electric power; why consider the little fuel cell as anything more than a laboratory curiosity?

In the first three decades of the twentieth century most of the emphasis of technological research in the power field was on the electromechanical generator. Fortunes were spent in bringing heat-driven power plants to their absolute maximum efficiency—still far less than half of perfect conversion of fuel to power. Only then did engineers begin to look about for better methods of producing electric power, and in the 1930's the old fuel cell was resurrected in England.

England had produced the first fuel cells, and by the late 1950's Francis T. Bacon—a descendant of the famous English philosopher and scientist Francis Bacon (1561–1626)—demonstrated a saw and a welding machine powered by a "Bacon cell," using hydrogen and oxygen to produce electricity. This "hydrox" cell made big news on both sides of

Golf cart powered by hydrazine fuel cell

the Atlantic, and researchers in America too were showing what it could do. A variety of equipment, including golf carts and tractors, was operated by bulky, expensive fuel cells, and producers of electric power were eying the device with mild interest. It was at this point that the space age boomed the fuel cell.

Industry is understandably interested in commercial applications, and a public utility has installed a fuel cell in one of its natural gas plants. A modification of the Apollo cell, this power supply is used only for a control panel but represents at least a foot in the utilities door for the fuel cell.

Dividing the practical results of all operating fuel cells

into the millions of dollars spent on research and development makes the new power supply seem terribly expensive. However, a careful look ahead indicates that the money is well spent.

For years we have been warned that we are rapidly using up the "fossil" fuels that nature stored up for us ages ago but is not replenishing. Coal, oil, and natural gas are not replaceable and when they are exhausted we must turn to nuclear power and solar power. Both these wonderful sources are around the corner in the future somewhere, but just when they can take over is problematical. In the meantime, any methods we can find for conserving our fossil fuels will help mightily. The fuel cell is just such a method. At a conversion efficiency of 80 per cent, it represents a saving of half our conventional fuels. That means stretching them out for twice as many years.

We have seen that a fuel cell is basically a simpler device than a steam generator or internal-combustion plant. It has another advantage over these methods: it is efficient even in small sizes. Homeowners may one day have their own "electric plant" in the utility room, converting gas or liquid fuel to electricity. Nuclear power plants must be even larger than the steam generator plants of today to be most efficient, thus ruling them out for small-area applications. Even after nuclear power is cheaply available, the fuel cell may be more desirable in many applications.

Another big job for the fuel cell is in the field of transportation. Years ago we had electric cars, but they gave way to gasoline engines. Now the pendulum may be about to swing back. Smog is a major problem in big cities today, and much of it is traceable to automobile exhausts. A fuel-cell-powered car produces no harmful exhaust gases. Water and carbon dioxide, the waste products from a fuel cell burning hydrocarbons, would be easily disposed of, or could even be recovered for some useful purpose. Elimination of smog would be enough incentive in itself, but there are many other advantages to the electric car.

These are glimpses of the fuel-cell world of tomorrow, a world with no smog or engine noise, one with fewer power-transmission wires to mar the landscape, and utility bills

Fuel cell built for Columbia Gulf for test use provides power for control panel

only a third of what they are today. It is the world of tomorrow, however, and one engineer has expressed it simply: "Don't order a fuel cell from me this year!"

Hydrogen, although cheaper than zinc, is still a lot more expensive than gasoline. And while researchers have demonstrated fuel cells operating on such hydrocarbons as gasoline and oil, these cells use platinum electrodes that few of us could afford for the family car. The fuel cell of today is still a relatively bulky affair. The Gemini power plant, for example, weighs 500 pounds complete with fuel for a fifteen-day mission and develops less than three horsepower. There is lots of work ahead for scientists and engineers.

Even so, there is sufficient promise for government and industry to drive ahead at full speed. And they have some more tricks up their sleeves, just in case. Already built and tested are bioelectric fuel cells in which bacteria convert everything from sugar to sea water, and sawdust to sewage, into electricity. Farther ahead are fantastic-sounding schemes for coupling fuel cells to nuclear plants and even solar energy converters to produce large amounts of cheap power.

From all indications, flight into deep space will one day be accomplished, not with rocket engines, but with electric propulsion—streams of ions ejected at tremendous speed. The fuel cell may well provide not just an auxiliary power supply but electric power for propulsion as well.

There's another aspect of the fuel cell that we've merely hinted at so far: its by-products. The fuel cell may be pressed into service as a double-duty device, giving us electric power plus a useful commodity, as a bonus. It may even turn into a prime tool for the chemical industry, producing such things as formic acid, acetic acids, and other chemicals.

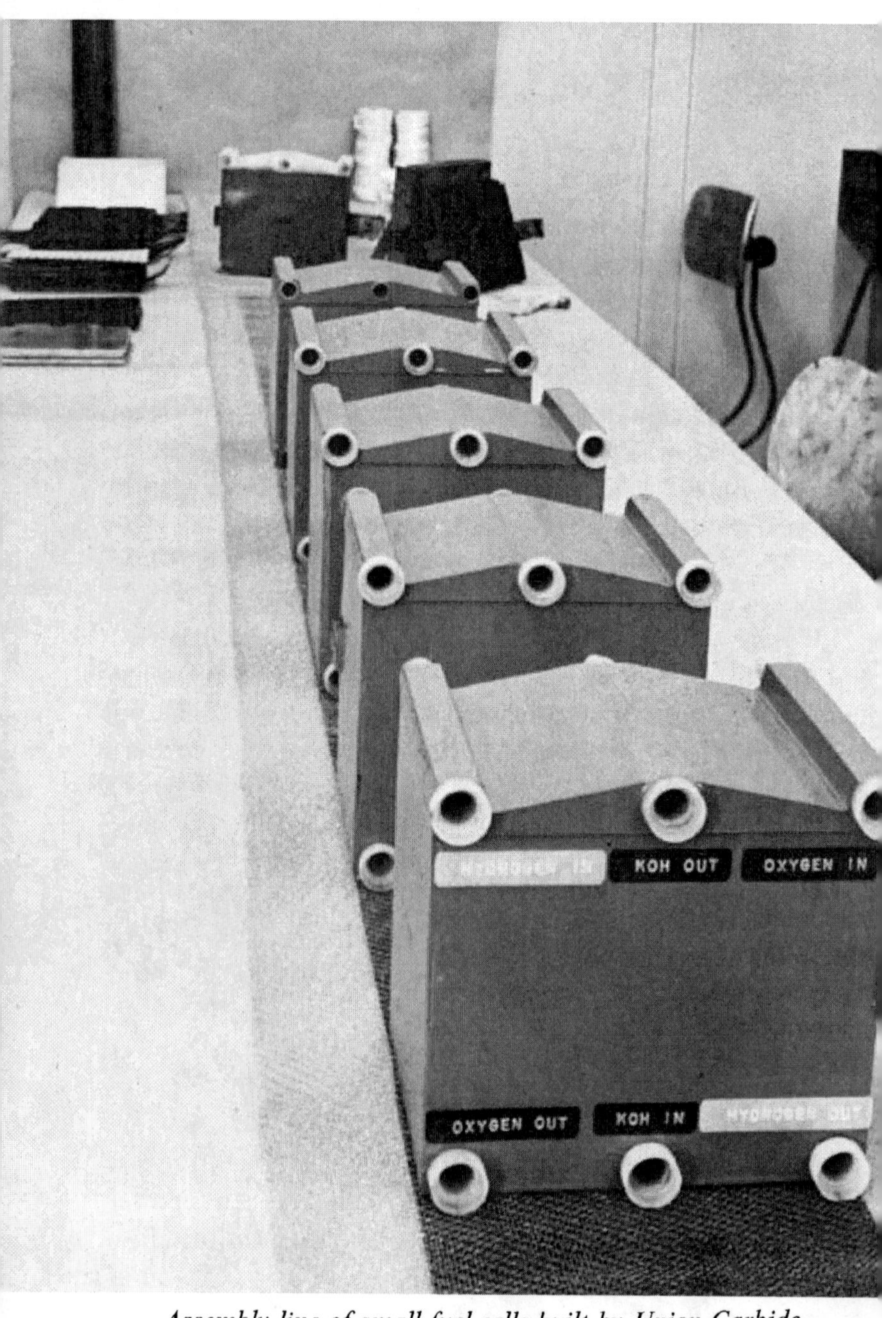

Assembly line of small fuel cells built by Union Carbide

One thing is certain: we are witnessing the beginning of a revolution in the power-production field. Einstein ushered in a noisier early revolution with a harmless-looking formula, $E = mc^2$. This new, quiet revolution springs from another formula that goes: $H_2 + \frac{1}{2} O_2 \xrightarrow{2e \text{ flow}} H_2O$, with the e standing for electricity.

CHAPTER TWO

History of the Fuel Cell

STRANGE TO SAY, the idea of the fuel cell really began with frog's legs. Late in the eighteenth century, Italian scientist Luigi Galvani accidentally discovered an odd twitching in the legs of a frog hung on a wire in his laboratory. Galvani mistakenly attributed the twitching to electricity generated by the frog's muscles, but a countryman, Alessandro Volta, soon corrected this error. Volta proved that it was actually the dissimilar metals the frog's legs had come in contact with that caused the current of electricity. Then he went on to invent the *voltaic cell,* in which two dissimilar metals created a tiny bit of electricity, and the *voltaic pile,* a number of cells interconnected to deliver greater power. Galvani's name also became part of the language of science in *galvanize, galvanometer,* and so on.

Scientists had been experimenting with electricity for many years. Static electricity was well known, and frictional electricity had been produced in large quantities. The Leyden jar could store electricity. Ben Franklin showed that lightning was the same kind of electricity as that produced in the laboratory. But Volta introduced a much handier way of generating the strange force that was so interesting to many experimenters. Here was chemically produced electricity, and, in England particularly, other researchers almost immediately began to extend Volta's work.

Sir Humphry Davy in 1802 developed a battery which, instead of using two metals or other solids to produce current, used carbon in contact with nitric acid. Davy (and two other researchers, Anthony Carlisle and William Nicholson) also used batteries to perform a strange experiment with water: an electric spark broke down the liquid into its components of hydrogen and oxygen. This "electrolysis" of water was important to the beginnings of the science of electrochemistry. Now, although no one had yet put the pieces together, all the preliminary steps for the fuel cell had been taken. It remained only for Sir William Grove in 1839 to build a totally new kind of electric battery, one fueled entirely by gases in the form of hydrogen and oxygen. Here was just the reverse of the electrolysis experiment of Carlisle and Nicholson. They had used electricity to split the water into gases; Grove put those gases back together to produce water—plus electricity!

Grove's first "gaseous voltaic battery" was described by him in *Philosophy Magazine* in February, 1839:

> ". . . over each piece of platinum was inverted a tube of gas, four-tenths of an inch in diameter, one of oxygen, the other of hydrogen. . . The instant the tubes were lowered so as to expose part of the surfaces of platinum to the gases, the galvanometer needle was deflected so strongly as to turn more than half round. . ."

Professor Grove ended his paper with the hope that with

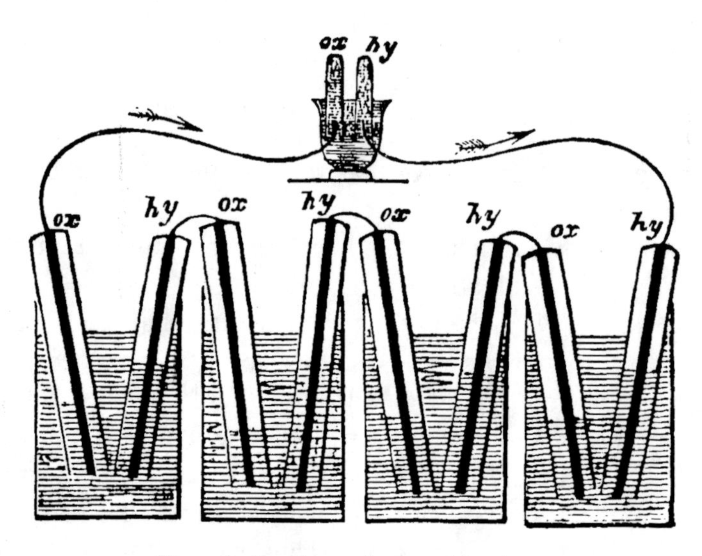

First fuel cells as depicted by Grove

his new battery he might "effect decomposition of water by means of its composition." As it turned out, his next experiments led to another kind of battery which was popular for a time, called a "Grove's battery." It was not until 1842 that Grove again reported on his pioneer fuel cell in *Philosophy Magazine*.

Suspecting that the area of exposed platinum was the key to the amount of electricity produced, Grove tried to use spongy, or porous electrodes—a technique that would later become standard in fuel cells. However, there were technical difficulties in preparing spongy platinum and Grove had to be content with flat platinum strips. He described the new battery in this way:

> "I therefore caused a series of fifty pairs to be constructed, the form and arrangement of which is given in the annexed figure, where *ox* denotes a tube filled with oxygen, *hy* one filled with hydrogen, and the dark line in the axis of the

tube platinized platina foil, which in the battery I constructed was about one-fourth of an inch wide. . . . The battery was charged with dilute sulphuric acid, sp. gr. 1.2, and the following effects were produced:—

1st. A shock was given which could be felt by five persons joining hands, and which when taken by a single person was painful.

2nd. The needle of a galvanometer was whirled around and stood at about 60°; with one person interposed in the circuit it stood at 40°, and was slightly deflected when two were interposed.

3rd. A brilliant spark visible in broad daylight was given between charcoal points. . ."

Grove pointed out that his battery was peculiar in having the current generated by gases, but this brilliant discovery was to amount to very little for more than a century. The production of hydrogen and oxygen gases was a very expensive process in those early days, and the special electrodes of platinum necessary to effect the conversion to electricity were costly. Even conventional voltaic batteries were just not able to compete economically with other power producers as was pointed out by scientist James Prescott Joule in a paper comparing electric batteries with a Cornish engine, the most efficient steam engine of that time:

"With my apparatus every pound of zinc consumed in a Grove's battery produces a mechanical force (friction included) equal to a weight of 331,400 lb. to the height of 1 foot, when the revolving magnets were moving at the velocity of 8 feet per second. Now the duty of the best Cornish steam-engine is about 1,500,000 lb. raised to a height of 1 foot by the combustion of a pound of coal, which is nearly five times the extreme duty that I was able to obtain from my electro-magnetic engine by the consumption of a pound of zinc. This comparison is so very unfavorable that I confess I almost despair of the success of electro-magnetic attractions as an economical source of power, for although my machine is by no means perfect, I do not see how the arrangement of its parts could be improved so far as to make the duty per pound of zinc superior to the duty of the best steam-engines per pound of coal. And even if this were attained, the expense of the zinc and the exciting fluids is so great, when compared with the price of coal, as to prevent the ordinary electro-magnetic engine from being useful for any but peculiar purposes."

Joule's conclusion made sense. A pound of zinc cost many times the price of a similar amount of coal; it was obvious that the "ordinary electro-magnetic engine" was not economical. However, another scientist, the German Alfred Mayer, writing in 1842, pointed out something about the heat engines of the day:

"By applying the principles which have been set forth to the relations subsisting between the temperature and the volume of gases, we find that the sinking of a mercury column by which a gas is compressed is equivalent to the quantity of heat set free by the compression, and hence it follows, the ratio of the capacity for heat of air under constant pressure and its capacity under constant volume being taken as 1.421, that the warming of a given weight of water from 0° to 1° C. corresponds to the fall of an equal weight from the height of about 365 meters. If we compare with this result the working of our best steam-engines we see how small a part only of the heat applied under the boiler is really transformed into motion or the raising of weights; and this may serve as justification for the attempts at the profitable production of motion by some other method than the expenditure of the chemical difference between carbon and oxygen—more particularly by the transformation into motion of *electricity obtained by chemical means.*" [I have added the italics for emphasis.]

Although Mayer's figure for the mechanical equivalent of heat was in error, here was a very keen analysis of the shortcomings of the heat engine, which is limited to the so-called Carnot-cycle efficiency. The Cornish engines were less than 10 per cent efficient. Even today, the best steam turbines deliver only about 40 per cent, and this seems to be the top limit. But Mayer's voice was raised in the wilderness of a technology geared to the exciting joining of the steam engine with the electrostatic generator to produce the dynamo. Inefficient as it was, the steam-driven dynamo produced great amounts of power; the potentially far more efficient fuel cell was lost in the great rush toward huge central power plants.

What was needed was an *extraordinary* electromagnetic engine, and it would be a century before it came along. Meantime, Sir William Grove achieved a measure of fame for his work with the electric light. His "peculiar" gaseous voltaic battery gathered dust, and it would be fifty years before other researchers continued the gaseous battery work.

Antoine Becquerel of France was a pioneer worker in the field of electrochemistry and in 1855 he attempted to make a new kind of battery. Becquerel melted niter in a vessel of platinum, placed a rod of carbon in this molten solution of salt, and obtained an electric current in wires attached to the carbon rod and the platinum vessel. His son Alexandre discovered a photoelectric effect in certain liquids—actually a forerunner of the solar battery so important today. To make the Becquerel family even more famous, Antoine, the grandson of the first Becquerel we mentioned, shared a Nobel Prize in 1903 with the Curies for the discovery of radioactivity.

By 1877 a researcher named Paul Jablochkov who was well-known for his inventions in the field of illumination (some early lamps of his design were called Jablochkov candles) put together a cell similar to that of Becquerel. Instead of the expensive platinum for a vessel, however, he used cast iron in an effort to make the device economical.

In 1889 two German-born scientists, Ludwig Mond and Carl Langer, took up the idea of the gas-powered battery, and called their device a fuel cell. The name embodied the importance of the concept, that of a battery with a replenishable fuel supply. Conventional batteries suffered the limitation that their electrodes were consumed more or less rapidly, after which they were of no use. To be sure, "secondary" batteries could be recharged by reversing the flow of current, but this was a troublesome and time-consuming process, during which the battery was of no service. Obviously, a battery to which fuel could be continuously added would have great advantages. There was also the matter of efficiency, touched on earlier by Mayer. Because of its chemical, rather than mechanical, conversion of fuel to electricity, the fuel cell is not doomed to relatively low efficiency as is the heat engine.

Grove had suggested the idea of porous electrodes to give more surface area for the electrochemical reaction. Mond and Langer simulated porous material by providing large electrodes consisting of a sheet of platinum pierced by many tiny holes. Separating the two electrodes was a "diaphragm" filled with diluted sulfuric acid. The gases used were hydrogen and oxygen, but the new fuel cell was far more powerful than that of Grove and produced a current of 2 amperes at 0.73 volt. Its efficiency in converting the gaseous fuel into electricity was approximately 50 per cent. Unfortunately, the large platinum electrodes were still so costly that the fuel cell could be afforded only by well-to-do researchers.

The steam-driven dynamo continued to ride high. Mond and Langer had a battery that was better than that of Grove, but not enough better. Again, interest in the fuel cell languished; who cared about a bulky, complicated laboratory toy that yielded infinitesimal amounts of electricity when there were dynamos available for producing many kilowatts?

The work of Mond and Langer was important, however. They had demonstrated the efficiency possible with the fuel cell and had also experimented with new electrolyte solutions. They suggested the use of cardboard and asbestos rather than metal in fuel cells, an idea that has recently been used successfully.

The great German chemist Wilhelm Ostwald, who would later win a Nobel Prize, in 1894 predicted an important future for electrochemistry. It would, he said, be instrumental in the development of inexpensive electricity. In particular he predicted ultimate success for the fuel cell using coal and air.

In 1896 Dr. William W. Jacques described just such experiments in producing electricity *directly* from coal. At that time coal was producing electricity, but in a roundabout way. As Jacques pointed out in *Harper's New Monthly Magazine:*

> "Much of the energy of combustion goes up the chimney as heat or smoke; much of the heat is lost in boiling the water to make steam; much of the expansive force of

the steam is wasted as it escapes from the engine; much of the power of the engine is wasted as friction; and there is some loss in the dynamo itself. Recent tests, made by a committee of the National Electric Light Association, of eighty modern electric light and power plants, show that the average plant wastes 97.4 per cent and utilizes as electricity only 2.6 per cent of the energy theoretically obtainable from coal."

While Dr. Jacques deplored such wasteful conversion of coal energy into electricity, he realized that electricity was the most convenient form of energy. From it man could easily get heat, light, mechanical action, or chemical force. The conversion of the energy locked in a lump of coal to *heat* was a far more efficient process than the production of electricity from the same source. Why couldn't a way be found to produce electricity as directly as heat was produced? Many men had dreamed of such a wonderful power plant as Dr. Jacques conjured up, sitting before his coal fire. But not many men did anything about converting the dream into reality.

First Jacques experimented with thermoelectricity, by placing wires or "thermocouples" directly in a flame. This yielded electricity, but only a tiny percentage of the potential in the coal. Next he tried making artificial lightning but this was not a practical scheme either. Jacques suggested that for all its seemingly furious power, a lightning bolt represents very little total power. For a fraction of a second it produces high power, but averaged over a length of time, a thunderstorm was about equal to the output of a bedroom fireplace.

Finally the experimenter hit on the idea of combining coal with oxygen, as occurs in the production of fire, but sup-

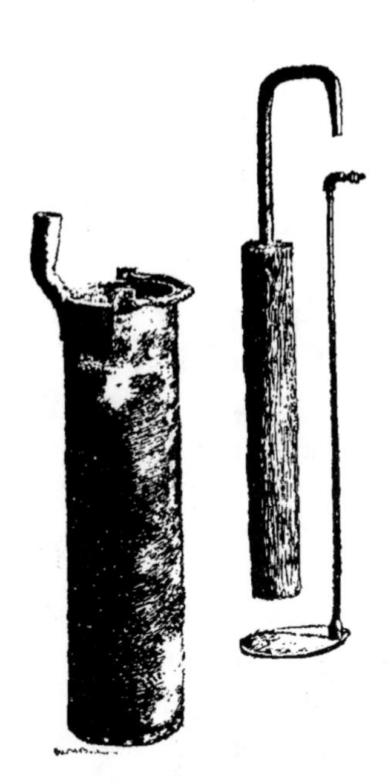

An elementary cell, as shown in Harper's Magazine *in 1896*

pressing actual flames and forcing the resulting energy to give itself up as electric current. Jacques placed coal in a container of liquid so that it could not burst into flame. Then he bubbled air through the liquid. In describing the resulting reaction Jacques used an accurate analogy:

> "We may picture each successive atom of oxygen, on its way from the source of the air supply through the liquid to the coal, as temporarily entering into chemical union with each of a row of atoms in the liquid, just as each successive man as he circles around in the 'grand right and left' of dancing temporarily clasps hands with each of the ladies of the set. When one substance passes through another in this way it furnishes a path in which an electric current can flow, so that by causing the oxygen to combine with the carbon through the intervening liquid opportunity

is furnished for an electric current to develop, and since combustion cannot take place, the chemical affinity of the coal for the oxygen is converted directly into electricity, and not into heat. Liquids which thus allow atoms of oxygen and a current of electricity to pass through them may be called 'electrolytic carriers.' "

Here, before the end of the nineteenth century, was the fuel cell carried in theory to its ultimate development. Instead of expensive hydrogen and oxygen, Jacques used coal, the cheapest fuel known, and air, which was free. Seemingly unaware of earlier work, by Becquerel and others, with the fuel cell, he claimed to have invented the device.

"I have thus discovered what I believe to be a new fact or principle not hitherto known to natural science—a principle which I hope may be as valuable to pure science as my invention promises to be to the useful arts."

Carbon electric generator made by Jacques

The first successful coal fuel cell was assembled in this manner: in a crucible of platinum, potash was melted over a coal fire. In the molten potash Jacques suspended a lump of coke by a platinum wire. Another wire was attached to the crucible, and the two wires were connected to a small electric motor. When air was blown into the potash electrolyte, the motor began to turn. An electromotive force of one volt and a current of several amperes were generated by the primitive device. Theoretically, the combination of carbon (coke) and oxygen (air) yields 1.04 volts.

Having demonstrated his invention on a small scale, Jacques went on to improve it. Because platinum was expensive, he found a way to treat iron and used it as his crucible. Crushing the coke, he powdered it and baked it in "sticks" about three inches in diameter and twenty inches long. Placing six of these "cells" in an airtight oven, he produced 2.16 horsepower to drive a sizable motor. About 1/10th horsepower was used to operate a pump to force air through the cells. Of the coal used, three parts were burned to heat the oven and two parts consumed in the fuel cell itself. Electricity produced from each pound of coal totaled 1,336 watt-hours, and Jacques proudly claimed that he had achieved an efficiency of 32 per cent, as compared with the 2.6 per cent yielded by steam-driven dynamos.

After the 2-horsepower fuel cell, he began construction of a more ambitious 40-horsepower power plant, enclosed in an oven ten feet square and six feet high. He admitted that there were problems to be overcome, including the fact that his molten potash electrolyte soon became so contaminated with carbonic acid that it had to be taken out and cleaned. "I believe it will be some time yet before the dynamo is rele-

Large carbon electric generator made by Jacques

gated to the attic with the spinning-wheel, or the wheels of the steam engine cease to operate," he said.

Jacques was right in this prediction. It would be more than half a century before any real progress would be made toward the world of direct-electricity conversion that he glowingly described, in which electric trains would be fuel-cell powered, as would giant ocean liners; we would heat and cook with electricity, and use it more in the metals industries; the fuel cell would revolutionize the chemical industry, and let us convert valueless material into compounds of great value. One advantage he wrote of in 1896 is even more marvelous today than when he set it down:

> "Then there is the advantage of comparatively pure air in our larger cities that would result from the absence of the smoke and soot of the millions of tons of coal now

burned. The difference between city air and the pure air of the country is largely, if not chiefly, due to the contamination by carbonic acid gas and smoke. Think of a smokeless London!"

Or Pittsburgh, or New York, or Los Angeles! Unfortunately for Dr. Jacques and all of us, his revolutionary new power plant was far from practical. He did not succeed in solving the problems of the electrolyte solution, and the iron he had prepared for his crucibles became contaminated during use. Instead of the dynamo or the steam engine being retired to the attic, it was Jacques's carbon-oxygen fuel cell that was forgotten, except by a few dedicated dreamers of direct conversion of electricity.

In 1921 Sir Eric Rideal presented a paper entitled "The Problem of the Fuel Cell" before the Faraday Society in London. He pointed out that electricity produced by boiler, steam engine and dynamo represented about 10 per cent of the fuel burned. If a gas engine and dynamo were used, efficiency as high as 25 per cent might be realized. This represented an increase in efficiency in the conventional methods of electric power production of some ten times since Dr. Jacques had written about his coal fuel cell. Unfortunately the fuel cell had made no such gains.

Sir Eric pointed out—as had Joule long before him—that while zinc might be converted into electricity electrochemically at an efficiency of 90 per cent, the relative costs of zinc and coal made such a power producer economical only in certain restricted applications. Much as England—and the world—might benefit from a practical fuel cell, such a device was not at hand or even around the corner.

In 1911 a British botanist named M. C. Potter had put

together a very strange sort of fuel cell. It was a "biochemical battery," consisting of yeast cultures and a suitable electrolyte. Surprisingly, it produced electricity. Not much, but enough to measure, and it did so through the action of living organisms. By and large, the scientific fraternity greeted Potter's work with stifled yawns. After all, it had long been known that living things produced electricity and a laboratory device producing only microwatts of power was merely an interesting curiosity. In 1930 the bio-battery idea was revived in the United States, but again there was little interest.

In 1932 Francis T. Bacon began to experiment in his laboratory with the century-old idea of the fuel cell. Hydrogen and oxygen gases were now cheaper and easier to obtain, and Bacon slowly improved the "hydrox cell" in which the two gases combine to produce water and electricity. World War II interrupted Bacon's work, but after the war he resumed it with vigor. He soon demonstrated a lift truck capable of handling two-ton loads, a circular saw, and a welding machine, each powered by a "Bacon cell."

Another Englishman, Dr. H. H. Chambers, was also working on the fuel cell during this period. Feeling that the hydrox cell demanded too costly a fuel, Chambers directed his work toward a cell that would operate on petroleum-base fuel and air, rather than hydrogen and oxygen.

In the United States too, fuel-cell research was going ahead rapidly. The Union Carbide Company built a fuel cell to power an Army radar set and the military became interested in the silence, efficiency, and simplicity of the device. Allis-Chalmers Manufacturing Company built fuel cells and powered farm tractors, lift trucks, and golf carts with them. The biochemical fuel cell was also rediscovered in the late

An early "Bacon cell"

1950's, and a number of firms began research and development of this strange device.

The fuel cell was long in coming, but now it was here at last. No mere laboratory curiosity, it became a space-age power supply that promised to live up to the predictions of its proponents in a variety of applications.

CHAPTER THREE

How the Fuel Cell Works

THE FUEL CELL is a device for converting fuel into electricity. To understand how it works, we must first know something about electricity, the flow of electrons through a conducting material. The Greeks gave us the words *electricity* and *electron* through their word *elektron,* for amber. The ancients noticed that when a piece of amber was rubbed with a cloth it exhibited an unexplainable attraction for small bits of material.

The Greeks also gave us the concept and the word *atom.* Democritus, in the fifth century B.C., theorized that there was a smallest unit of matter which he called the atom from a Greek word meaning indivisible. We now know, of course, that the particles which we call atoms can be further divided into many smaller particles. Each atom consists of a nucleus surrounded by electrons, a sort of miniature solar system with central sun and orbiting planets. Physicists continue to break the nucleus down into even further subdivisions, but we shall consider only the nucleus, and the electrons that encircle it.

Electrons are negatively charged particles. The nucleus

is positively charged, and the result is a balancing of electric charges so that normally the atom is electrically neutral. However, atoms can be "excited," or raised to an energy level above their normal state, in a number of ways. Atoms may be heated, for example, or bombarded with high-speed particles. When this happens, it is possible for the delicately held electrons to be jolted out of their orbits and separated from the atoms; it is also possible for additional electrons to be given to the atom. An atom that loses or gains an electron is said to be "ionized." "Ion" comes from the Greek word meaning "wanderer."

Electrons, we see, are able under certain conditions to move from one atom to another. These "free" electrons are what make up the flow of electricity. Electrons move more readily in some materials than others. Those materials that permit free movement we call conductors, because they conduct electrons easily from one atom to another. Those materials that do not allow such free movement are called nonconductors, or insulators.

Silver is an excellent conductor because it permits easy movement of free electrons from atom to atom. This movement is not a continuous travel from one end of the conductor to the other of the same electron. Rather, it is like that of waves on the ocean. Water does not move very far in this phenomenon, but each wave transfers some motion to the next and the effect is of moving waves that travel miles across the sea to break on a distant shore. Another analogy is the old-time "bucket brigade" at a fire. A free electron leaves one atom and attaches itself to the next. This action knocks an electron out of the second atom, and it in turn looks for a new home. No single electron moves very far, but

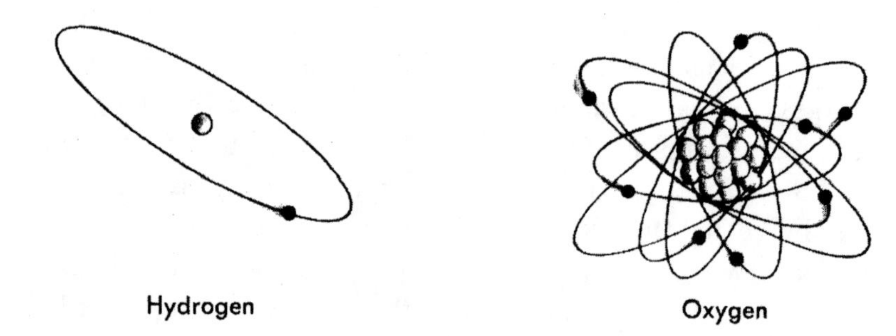

Artist's drawing of hydrogen and oxygen atoms, showing electrons

the resulting current of electricity moves very rapidly through the conductor.

What happens in a piece of glass? Instead of promoting the movement of free electrons, the atomic structure of glass (an excellent insulator) makes such movement nearly impossible. Under sufficient electrical pressure, insulators will break down and pass electrons, but this is not an easy path for current.

Thus far we have seen that it is possible for free electrons to move through a conductor in a "bucket brigade" fashion. Now let us see what it is that determines the direction in which this motion will be, and how much electric current results. We know that water will flow under certain conditions. In the simplest case it will flow downhill, under the pull of gravity. We can also cause it to flow by creating pressure with a pump. Electrical pressure is commonly called "voltage," in honor of Volta. Voltage is also known as "electromotive force" or "electrical potential."

Suppose we have two containers of water under equal pressure, and we connect them with a pipe. There will be no flow of water because there is no driving force to cause such a flow. The same is true of electricity. It does not flow spontaneously through a conductor. There must be a difference in potential, or voltage, from one end of the conductor to the other. Ionized atoms can possess a positive or a negative charge of electricity, depending on whether they have lost or gained electrons. If we connect positively charged material with negatively charged material by means of a length of conducting wire, what will happen? Just as pressurized water flows toward lower pressure, electrons flow toward lesser electrical pressure.

There is an old saying that "opposites attract." This is another way of describing electric current flow between materials at different potential. Negative electrons flow from a negatively charged body to one with a positive charge, until each body is at the same potential. The simplest demonstration of this is the action in a chemical battery, or voltaic cell.

Both Volta and Galvani were accorded the honor of having their names become part of electrical terminology. The volt is the unit of electromotive force. Galvanic action is the phenomenon of current flow from bodies at different potentials. A galvanic or electromotive series is a listing of materials in order of their electrical charge or potential. Galvani found that contact between brass and iron caused a flow of current (although he misinterpreted the phenomenon). Most dissimilar metals will cause such a current, its strength depending on how far apart the materials are on the galvanic scale. You can detect the weak flow of current between orange juice and an aluminum pan by touching to your tongue wires in contact with those materials. Volta used this "human current detector" in his experiments and gave himself severe jolts of electricity. Nowadays we use an instrument called a galvanometer to detect the flow of current.

Below is a list of materials arranged in electromotive series. You may have had experience with corrosion resulting from placing two of them in contact with each other. Aircraft builders have learned that magnesium and aluminum when riveted together cause a galvanic action, particularly in salt air. This unwanted "battery" simply eats away one of the "electrodes" without performing a useful function.

ELECTROMOTIVE SERIES

MAGNESIUM	2.40 volts	
ALUMINUM	1.70	
ZINC	0.76	
IRON	0.44	
TIN	0.14	
HYDROGEN	0.00	(Hydrogen is used
COPPER	−0.34	as a standard
OXYGEN	−0.40	reference electrode)
SILVER	−0.80	
GOLD	−1.36	

The higher the material is in the series, the more readily it will give up its free electrons.

Let us now look at a simple "primary battery." We have seen that all we need are two dissimilar metals to cause a flow of electrons, or electricity. However, we can hasten the flow by means of an "electrolyte," or intervening fluid between the "electrodes," or dissimilar materials. Just as salt water quickens the corrosion of magnesium and aluminum on aircraft flying over or near the ocean, so selected electrolytes increase the effectiveness of the primary battery.

Volta used zinc and copper in his battery. Today most primary batteries use zinc, but carbon has been substituted for the copper. An electrolyte of sulfuric acid and water has been added to make a stronger battery. Let us analyze what happens when we bring these three materials into contact.

Until we connect the two electrodes by short-circuiting them, or through an external circuit such as a flashlight bulb, a motor, or some other user of electric current, nothing happens within the battery. When we do make the connection, two related actions take place: (1) there is a chemical reaction between the elements of the battery, and (2) there is a

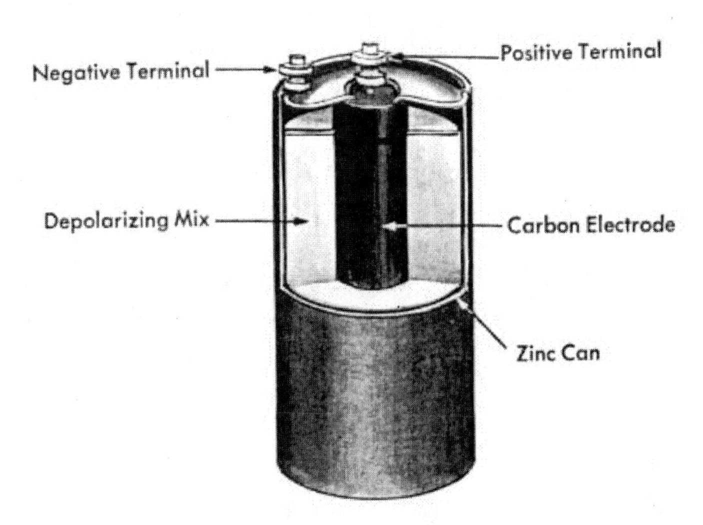

Cutaway drawing of a simple battery

flow of electrons through the external circuit. The chemical reaction in our simple battery is expressed this way:

$$Zn + H_2SO_4 + H_2O \longrightarrow ZnSO_4 + H_2O + H_2 \uparrow$$

In plain English, this means that the zinc, sulfuric acid, and water combine to form zinc sulfate and water plus hydrogen. Notice that the carbon does not take part in the chemical reaction but serves only as a path for the flow of electrons. However, the zinc, which is usually in the form of the outer case of the battery, is slowly consumed by the process. Zinc is thus the "fuel" that is "burned" to produce electricity.

As zinc is "oxidized," the second reaction occurs. Within the electrolyte, ions are formed. We remember that ions are atoms that have acquired a positive or negative charge. We have both types in the battery. The positive ions are hydrogen ions and they are attracted to the carbon electrode. Something must attract them, of course, and it is negative zinc ions formed by the combination of electrons that have traveled from the carbon electrode through the external circuit to combine with the zinc atoms at the zinc electrode.

Not surprisingly, some of the reactions that take place in the battery are not particularly helpful in the production of electricity. One such is called "polarization." During the flow of current in the battery, bubbles of hydrogen are formed on the carbon electrode. Not only do these bubbles suppress the desired chemical reaction and electron flow, they also set up an electromotive force or voltage in the opposite direction from that desired. If something is not done to lessen the effects of polarization, the battery soon becomes completely polarized and useless. To prevent this, a depolarizing agent is used.

In a dry cell a substance called manganese dioxide is added at the carbon electrode. This supplies free oxygen that combines with the hydrogen bubbles to produce water, plus another form of manganese oxide. Since hydrogen bubbles are not permitted to build up, depolarization of the electrode does not occur, or is postponed at least for a period of time.

Here, then, is the simple primary battery. It is a very useful producer of electricity in small amounts, even though zinc is an expensive fuel. However, there is a disadvantage in the primary battery that should immediately be obvious: it is an expendable device. Like a skyrocket or a Roman candle, it burns itself up in the process of doing its job. Worn out primary batteries are of no use except perhaps as scrap. When flashlight batteries burn out, we discard them, preferably before they corrode and swell up to stick in the flashlight.

Volta's pioneering voltaic pile was a "dry" battery. Later batteries were "wet," as a liquid electrolyte was added for better performance. A wet battery has several inconvenient aspects, and the popular "LeClanché" cell uses an electrolyte that is actually in paste form so it won't leak.

Inventors were not long in developing the "secondary" battery. The LeClanché cell depends on a chemical action that is irreversible, or one-way. There are, however, reversible chemical actions that produce electricity as a by-product. The automobile battery is a secondary battery. It is a lead-acid type and this is the chemical reaction that takes place:

$$Pb + PbO_2 + 2H_2SO_4 \underset{\leftarrow \text{ charging}}{\overset{\text{discharging} \rightarrow}{\longleftrightarrow}} 2PbSO_4 + 2H_2O$$

Notice that the arrows point both ways. This means that the chemical action is reversible. As we call on the battery for electricity, current flows through the external circuits and the acid in the electrolyte is used to produce lead sulfate. When the generator begins to charge the battery, electrons flow in the reverse direction, and as a result the lead sulfate is changed back to lead. The advantages of a secondary, or rechargeable battery are obvious. However, there are still some disadvantages, for an external generator of some kind is needed to perform the recharging action. Also, the secondary battery will not last forever, as we know from buying replacement automobile batteries.

Now, having surveyed conventional batteries, let's consider the "battery with a gas tank," the fuel cell. If there is a single word that best describes the difference between the fuel cell and the dry cell, that word is "invariance." The electrodes of the dry cell vary with time; in an ideal fuel cell the electrodes and electrolyte do not vary, but remain in the same condition they were in when the electrochemical reaction began.

The Fuel Cell

We know that experimenters long ago used electricity from a voltaic battery to electrolyze water, breaking it down into its two gaseous components hydrogen and oxygen. Later, Sir William Grove reversed the process, and recombined the two gases to produce water again, plus a quantity of electricity. (He used the electricity, incidentally, to electrolyze more water.) This, basically, is the operation of the fuel cell. As long as fuel is added, electricity is produced. Let's look at the similarities between a conventional battery and the fuel cell.

A fuel cell, like a dry cell, has two electrodes, one negative and the other positive. Separating these electrodes is the now-familiar electrolyte, that aids conversion of fuel into electricity. To one electrode we add the fuel, in the form of hydrogen. To burn fuel we need an "oxidant," and so we add oxygen to the other electrode. What happens next is similar to the chemical reaction in the primary battery.

In the fuel cell, hydrogen in the electrode reacts with oxygen ions from the electrolyte solution to form water and to release free electrons in the process. These electrons flow from the fuel electrode into the external circuit to operate whatever equipment is connected, and then back to the oxygen electrode, just as in the primary battery. Now we need

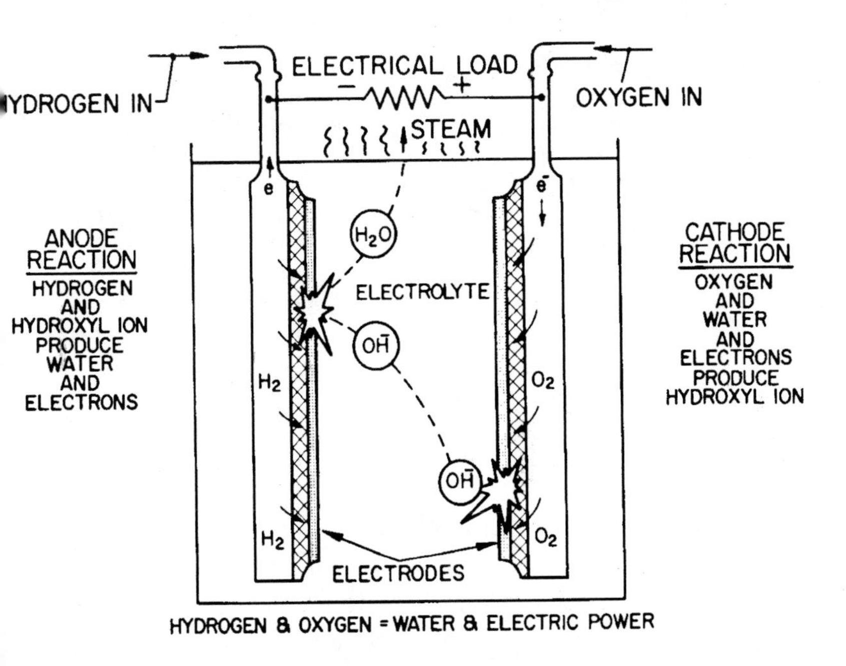

Basic fuel cell

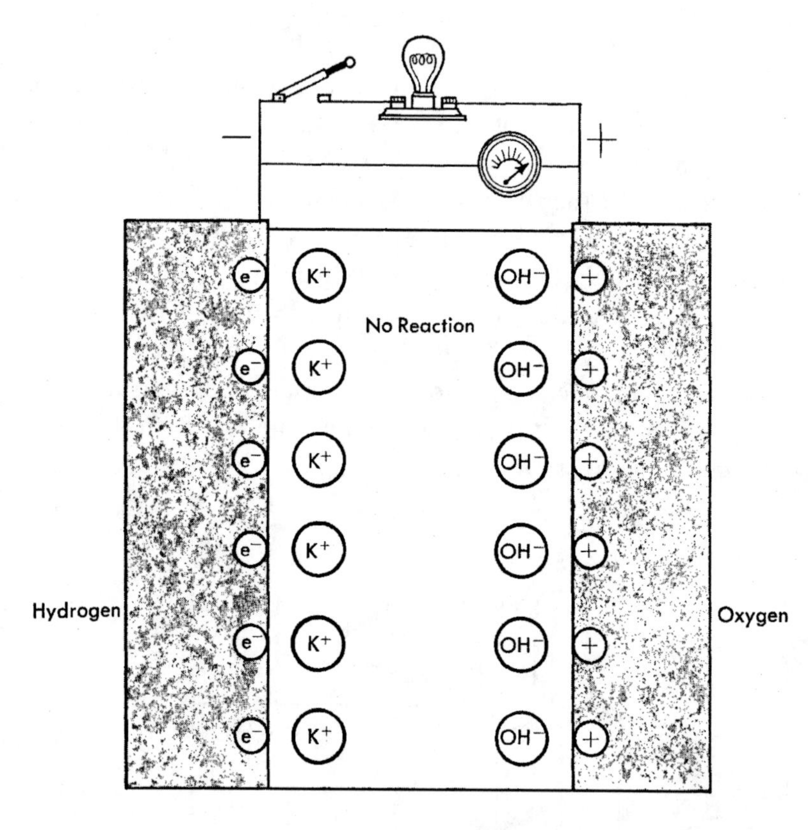

Fuel cell will not produce electricity until circuit is closed.

replacements for the electrons flowing out of the fuel electrode, so the electrons returning by way of the oxygen electrode combine with oxygen and the water in the electrolyte to form hydroxyl ions. These ions travel across the electrolyte to the fuel electrode, and the current of electrons continues merrily on its way. All very simple, but in practice

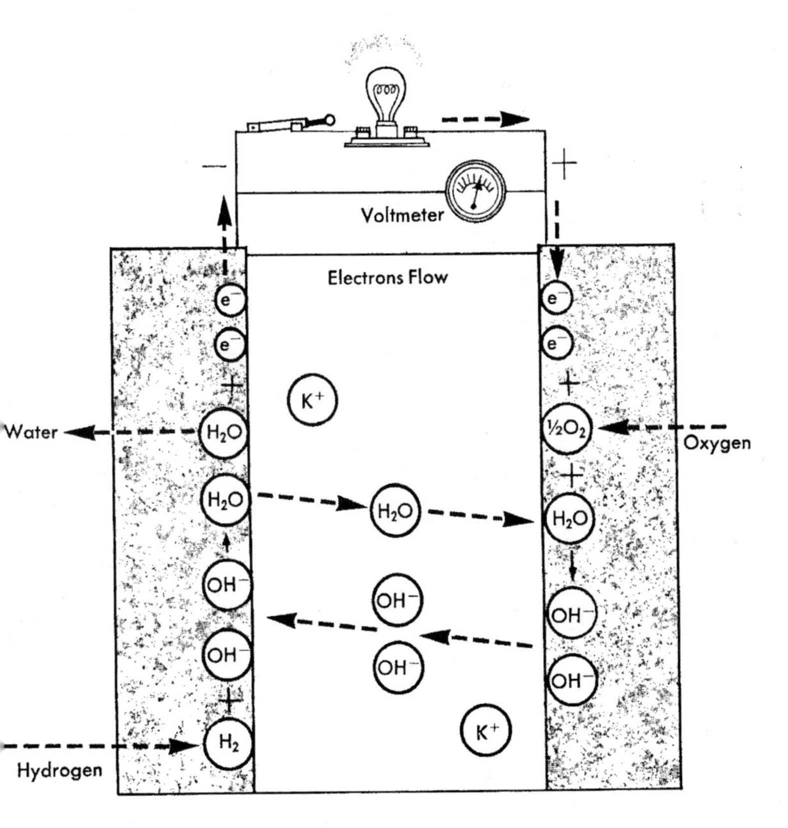

Circuit closed. Cell produces water and electricity, lighting bulb.

far more difficult than it sounds. In chemical sign language, here is how the over-all reaction looks:

$$H_2 + \frac{1}{2} O_2 \xrightarrow{\text{2e flow}} H_2O$$

We have simplified the reaction that takes place in the fuel cell to make it easier to grasp. Actually, the chemical reaction takes place in steps. When a molecule of hydrogen (containing two atoms) enters the fuel electrode, it is first broken into two "chemisorbed" atoms (atoms which attach themselves to the catalyst on the electrode). It is the job of the catalyst to increase the desired electrochemical reaction. In the next step, hydroxyl ions from the electrolyte combine, again with the help of the catalyst, with single hydrogen atoms. They form water, with a free electron left over to begin its trip through the external circuit. Because the two electrodes are at a different electrical potential, free electrons flow to the positively charged (oxygen) electrode. The reaction at the fuel electrode is:

$$H_2 + 2OH^- \longrightarrow 2H_2O + 2e$$

At the oxygen electrode a more complex reaction takes place than at the fuel electrode. Oxygen molecules join with electrons entering the oxygen electrode from the external circuit, and with water molecules from the electrolyte. The results are two kinds of ions, hydroxyl and "perhydroxyl." The perhydroxyl ion must be further broken down into a hydroxyl ion for transport back across to the fuel electrode, plus a free oxygen atom for use in subsequent oxidation processes. Another catalyst is used to effect this breakdown. The oxygen electrode reaction is:

$$\tfrac{1}{2}O_2 + H_2O + 2e \longrightarrow 2OH^-$$

We know that the electrons produced give the desired electric current for operating equipment. What of the water that is also formed? It may go into solution in the electrolyte, or it may be removed from the fuel electrode as it is formed.

Let's now consider some other aspects of the operation of the fuel cell. Suppose we open the switch in the external circuit; that is, we no longer draw any current from the fuel cell. Does the electrochemical reaction still take place? As in the dry cell, it does not, and this is one of the great advantages of the fuel cell as compared with mechanical power producers. It generates electricity *only when needed.*

When no current is being drawn, the fuel electrode accumulates a layer of negative charges at its surface that attract positive ions. At the oxygen electrode there are positive charges that attract negative ions (hydroxyls). The resulting films form a barrier to any further reaction. When we close the switch in our external circuit, the negative charges do not accumulate, but move out through the circuit and the reaction between gases and electrolyte solution again takes place.

Having examined the over-all reaction in the fuel cell, we shall now look at each component in more detail. All of these are vital, but for convenience we shall discuss them in the following order: fuels, oxidants, electrodes, electrolytes, and catalysts.

Fuels

Sir Humphry Davy used a metal-acid combination in his fuel cell; Grove used two gases. Since then a great number of materials have been used in attempts to find better fuels and oxidants for the fuel cell. Metals are easy to use, as proved by the popularity of zinc in dry cells.

A pound of zinc occupies a very small volume. The same energy in hydrogen gas requires many cubic feet of space. Thus the fuel tank for a hydrogen-oxygen fuel cell poses a problem. It is possible to compress a gas, but this means the expense of strong metal tanks, extra weight, and so on. Hydrogen can be liquefied to reduce its volume further, but this raises problems of high pressure and extremely low temperature.

For several reasons, liquid metals are good prospects for

fuel cells, and many combinations have been tried. In a later chapter we shall see the advantages of metals that can be pumped and otherwise circulated in a fuel-cell system.

Having mentioned liquid metals, we move on to simple liquids. Gasoline is obviously a very handy fuel. It has low volume per unit of energy delivered, and it is very cheap. Compared with hydrogen gas in carload lots at bargain prices, gasoline is still only about one-tenth as costly. Why not use gasoline or kerosene in a fuel cell? Some day we may do so, but for the present we do not know how to oxidize these liquids directly in a fuel cell to produce electricity. Instead we resort to a two-step process in which the gasoline is "re-formed" into hydrogen gas and then fed to the fuel cell.

More success has been achieved with other liquids, including ammonia, glycerine, ethylene glycol, and methanol, or wood alcohol. These fuels cost more than gasoline for equivalent energy production, but it is possible to utilize them directly in the fuel cell.

There are cheaper gases than pure hydrogen, and many of these have been used to fuel fuel cells. Among them are methane (the gas produced by fermentation of bacteria), propane (the familiar bottled gas many of us use for cooking and heating), and natural gas. Even coal can be used by first converting it into coal gas in a reformer like that of the gasoline system.

Oxidants

We know the high cost of hydrogen as a fuel, and we should remember that pure oxygen is costly too. For this reason researchers also seek cheaper oxidants for fuel cells. One quite obvious possibility is air, which is free for the taking. Air is not pure oxygen, however, and its use results in a less efficient reaction within the fuel cell. However, the best solution will perhaps be a compromise, and the "methanol-air" fuel cell seems a good possibility for an economical power plant. Chlorine is about the only other practical oxidant, and it is not used except for special applications.

Electrodes

After fuels and oxidants, our next consideration is that of electrodes. Here the problem is one of increasing the reactivity of the fuel and oxidant within the cell. Porous electrodes (which Grove suggested) are used to increase the area available for reaction. Many different materials have been tried, and electrode research represents a costly part of the work on fuel cells.

Carbon electrodes are used in low-temperature hydrogen-oxygen fuel cells. Carbon is inert, and can be made so porous that a one-centimeter cube of the material offers a reaction area of 1,000 square centimeters! However, carbon has disadvantages too. It is subject to "drowning" of the pores by water formed in the electrolyte. "Flooding" by the electrolyte is a problem too, although not as serious as that of drowning. Carbon is also not as strong as is desirable. For these reasons, metallic electrodes are often used. The Bacon cell uses porous nickel electrodes instead of carbon electrodes. Stainless steel is also used.

An unusual and very effective electrode has been developed. German scientists "sintered," or made porous, an alloy of nickel and aluminum. This sintered material was then treated electrochemically to dissolve away the aluminum, leaving many hollow spaces within the electrode and offering much surface area for reaction. Because of the way these electrodes are made they have been named "double-skeleton" or DSK.

Evidence of the progress made in fuel-cell technology is seen in some electrodes now mass-produced. These are only 0.025 inch in thickness and help materially to reduce the size of individual cells and thus the size of the complete battery of many cells.

Electrolyte

In the ordinary wet cell, sulfuric acid and water are used as the electrolyte through which ion exchange occurs. In fuel cells various liquids are used. Most popular is potassium hydroxide. The "aqueous," or liquid, electrolyte has the advantages of low internal resistance and easily available ionic oxygen for the needed reactions.

Not all electrolytes are aqueous, and for some high-temperature fuel cells molten salts are used. A more recent innovation is the solid electrolyte, in which a thin "ion-exchange membrane" of plastic resin takes the place of liquid or molten salt. This membrane permits movement of ions, while preventing transport of other particles. While it has higher resistance to ion flow than the liquid electrolyte, the membrane is much thinner.

Advantages of the solid electrolyte include easier rejection of water formed in the fuel-cell reaction, and less susceptibility to problems of a weightless environment. This latter factor is of importance in space applications, as we shall see later on.

Catalysts

The factor of "reactivity" is of prime importance in the

fuel cell. The rate of reaction governs the amount of power produced, and to hasten the complex reactions at the interface between electrode and electrolyte it is necessary to add catalytic substances. These catalysts are the subject of much study. Among early materials used was platinum, a very expensive material. The catalyst (1) attracts the fuel molecules to the electrode surface, (2) splits the molecules for migration to the reaction point, and (3) reduces the activation energy necessary to produce the reaction. Other noble (highly corrosion resistant) metals, including rhodium, palladium, and ruthenium, plus their alloys, are used as catalysts.

Just as polarization plagues the dry cell, it is an unwanted reaction in the fuel cell. Various catalytic techniques are used to "depolarize" the electrodes so that voltage is not reduced seriously.

The Fuel Cell in Action

Let's backtrack and take a fresh approach to the amazing ability of hydrogen and oxygen to combine into water and electricity. Actually this combination can properly be called "burning," and it takes place because each of the gases separately possesses more energy than the compound H_2O, or water. It is something like the phenomenon of difference in potential we discussed earlier. Energy runs downhill toward a state of equilibrium. But there are a few barriers in the way of such reactions that prevent complete chaos.

Hydrogen and oxygen heated together to 500° C. will not merely burn, they will explode. If this explosion could occur at room temperature, handling such gases would be more dangerous than it is. Fortunately, we must raise the energy level of the gases to "ignite" them, much as we have to heat wood or paper or other fuel to the kindling point before oxidation takes place. Once started, the reaction will continue as long as there is fuel, an oxidant, and proper temperature.

The electrochemical reaction in the fuel cell, once set in motion, releases more energy than was needed to start the process. Engineers call this kind of reaction "exothermic." If the reaction did not yield more energy than it took to cause it, it would be "endothermic," and hardly of use to the fuel-cell designer.

In the fuel cell, then, we are actually burning a fuel. This fuel is commonly hydrogen gas, and the oxidant, oxygen. To surmount the safety barrier nature provides, we use the catalysts mentioned earlier. Now a reaction between the two materials can take place, but not as an explosion or heat. Instead, the burning produces an electric current. If we provide an easy path for this current by short-circuiting the fuel cell with a low-resistance wire, what will happen? The result is not desirable; something like opening the floodgates of a dam instead of letting the water run out through a turbine to extract its energy efficiently.

If we short-circuit the fuel cell, energy escapes very rapidly. As the reaction rate increases, the temperature in the cell increases too. The hotter the fuel cell gets, the less efficient a generator of electricity it is. So we provide a proper high-resistance load on the fuel cell and keep the heat of reaction low. Thus most of the fuel is converted, not into heat, but directly into electricity.

In theory, a fuel cell can approach 100 per cent efficiency. In other words, from a given amount of fuel we get the equivalent amount of electricity, with no loss incurred during the conversion process. In practice, this ideal has not been reached, however. The energy barrier represents some loss,

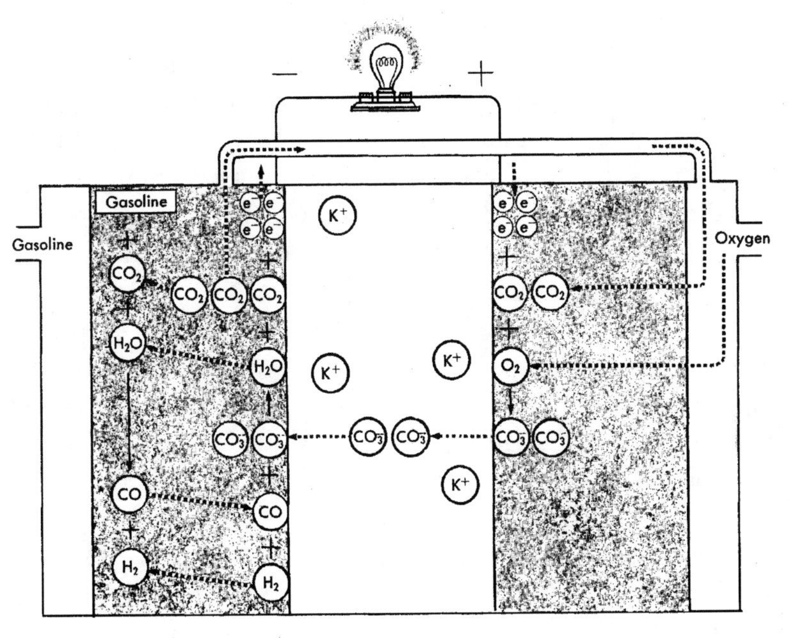

High-temperature fuel cell, using gasoline, produces electrons, water, and carbon dioxide.

or "friction." So does the production of any heat. However, 75 per cent efficiency is realistic for the fuel cell, and it may be possible to better this figure. When we compare this with the over-all efficiency of conventional energy converters, the advantages of the fuel cell are obvious.

Toward Better Fuel Cells

The fuel cell we have used as our model is the hydrogen-oxygen or "hydrox" fuel cell. Bacon came to the conclusion that at room temperature and pressure the hydrox cell would not be practical as a producer of appreciable amounts of power. For example, a fuel cell with a cubic foot of volume produces only about one kilowatt-hour of electricity, or enough to run a one-horsepower motor about an hour and twenty minutes. So Bacon set out to improve the hydrox cell.

At atmospheric pressure, the gases just percolate through the electrodes, leisurely producing electrons. Suppose we pump the gases in, thought Bacon. And suppose we heat up the fuel cell to about 250° C., instead of 25° C.? He got busy and built the Bacon cell, operating at 250° C., and a pressure of 800 pounds per square inch. Now he had a device operating at ten times the temperature and more than fifty times the pressure. Although its output was not fifty times that of the old fuel cell, nor even ten, it was a creditable six times the power per unit of weight.

One classification of fuel cells depends on their operating temperature. A low-temperature fuel cell operates below about 120° C.; the intermediate cell up to about 900° C. and the very-high-temperature cell from 900° C. to higher temperatures.

The low-temperature hydrox fuel cell is one of the simplest designs. It also offers the advantage of producing water as a by-product, and in such applications as power plants for spacecraft, weight-free drinking water is a welcome bonus. However, it is obvious that for the fuel cell to become broadly economical, cheaper fuels, oxidants, electrolytes, electrodes, and catalysts are going to be needed.

While hydrogen and oxygen can be made to combine at low temperatures, cheaper hydrocarbon fuels do not. To operate a fuel cell on gasoline or other petroleum products requires temperatures higher than 500° C. This means vastly more complicated problems with materials used for electrodes and catalysts. Moreover, the fuel must be converted into hydrogen and carbon monoxide before it is burned with the oxygen. Because of these and other problems, the high-

Individual fuel cells, like the one shown here, are assembled in series to meet the voltage requirement.

temperature, low-cost hydrocarbon fuel cell cannot yet compare with the hydrox fuel cell for power output per weight.

The fuel cell is a marvelous energy converter, but it is not the perfect solution to all power needs. In the next chapter we will look more closely at the good points of the device, and also at its drawbacks.

CHAPTER FOUR

The Balance Sheet

Now that we know what the fuel cell is and how it operates, perhaps we can begin to understand why it is so interesting to scientists and engineers all over the world. There are many reasons for the recent and rapid development of the fuel cell from laboratory curiosity to practical power supply. One big one, as we have pointed out, is efficiency.

We saw in the preceding chapter that in theory the fuel cell can approach 100 per cent efficiency in its direct conversion of fuel into electricity. This perfect figure is an unattainable goal; however, careful analysis of fuel-cell capabilities shows that actual efficiency as high as 96 per cent is feasible and that 75 per cent is easily attainable with hydrox cells. Experimental fuel cells burning cheap fuel have already delivered better than 40 per cent. Even this 40 per cent figure is exciting to engineers, when they compare it with conventional power converters.

The best of our large-scale electric power plants convert only 40 per cent or less of the energy in coal or oil into electricity. This seemingly poor performance is inescapable for several reasons that we shall now examine in detail. The

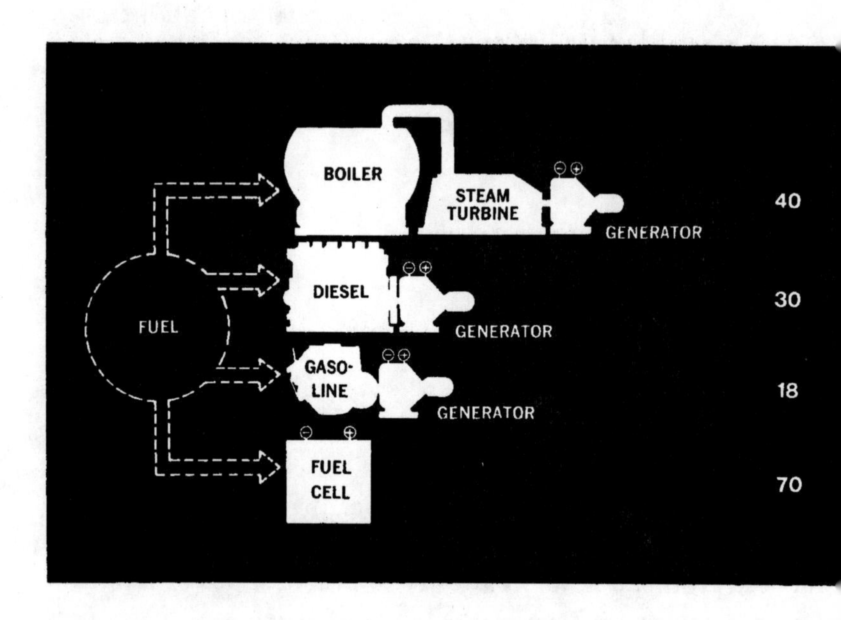

Over-all efficiency of fuel cell compared with other power sources

steam-turbine electric plant does not produce electricity in a single step as does the fuel cell. Instead there are several successive steps, and each takes its toll in the form of power loss. Assuming we start with 100 units of energy, how much do we end up with as electricity in the power lines, and where and why do we lose the rest?

First of all, coal or oil is burned to heat a water boiler to produce steam. This combustion process is not perfect, and only about 90 of our energy units get from the fuel into the steam. Next the steam (containing 90 units of heat energy) drives a turbine. Even though this engine represents the best mechanical design and construction possible today, more than half of our 90 energy units are wasted in this step because of thermodynamic laws concerning waste heat. Let's take a minute to look into something called the "Carnot principle."

A young French engineer, Sadi Carnot, in 1824 wrote a small book that later became the basis for the science of thermodynamics. One of the resulting laws governs the maximum possible efficiency of any engine operating on heat:

$$\text{Carnot efficiency} = \frac{T_1 - T_2}{T_1},$$

where T represents absolute temperature (temperature above absolute zero).

Let's translate this into some numbers from our example above. Steam enters our turbine at an absolute temperature of 1100° and is exhausted at 500°. Thus T_1 is 1100° and T_2 is 500°. Substituting these in the formula, we find a Carnot efficiency of 600/1100, or only 55 per cent. This is not the result of poor design; if engineers could do better they would. But there is no practical way to increase intake temperature without melting the engine, or to lower the exhaust temperature. (A temperature of 40°F. is equal to 500° absolute.) We are stuck with such losses unless someday we can operate our engines at much higher temperatures. Meantime, our 90 units of energy have shrunk now to 49.5 units.

The Carnot loss, unfortunately, is not the only loss we suffer in the turbine. There are unavoidable losses including friction and sound, amounting to about 15 per cent and further cutting our remaining energy to about 42.5 units. In the generator, which converts the rotary motion of the turbine shaft into electricity, there is another slight loss of about 5 per cent and this shrinks our energy to about 40 per cent.

Even this is not the final loss, since we still have to put the electricity into a power line and send it miles to the users, losing another few per cent in the process. For every three pounds of coal or gallons of oil we burn, then, conventional systems turn only about one pound into useful power.

Now let's look at the fuel cell. At worst, it matches the maximum practical efficiency of the steam electric plant. At best, fuel-cell efficiency may be double; this means we produce power at half the cost and save fuels that are ever getting scarcer. The fuel cell is different from a steam-turbine generator in respects other than efficiency. It is a single unit, rather than a combination of burner, boiler, turbine, and generator. There is no flame and there are no moving parts to wear, create friction, and need lubrication. There is no (or at worst, very little) waste heat to be dumped, no noise, no noxious exhaust, no soot, no boiler to burst, no fire danger, and no steam to scald anyone. We pour or pump fuel and oxidant in, and out comes electricity.

There is another advantage in the fuel cell that is not so readily apparent. The steam-electric plant we have been describing is a large-scale installation, a multi-megawatt producer of power representing a very large investment in capital. Suppose we want to build a small steam generator for several kilowatts—what efficiency can we expect? Not 40 per cent, but half that or even less. The fuel cell, on the other hand, is just as efficient in small sizes as large, and its economic advantage increases rapidly in competition with conventional power producers as size of the required plant goes down.

We mentioned that the fuel cell is quiet, and in many applications this advantage is tremendous. For example, one of the first uses of fuel-cell power in a practical test was to operate a portable radar set for the United States Army. Called the "Silent Sentry," this power pack is obviously less obtrusive than a noisy diesel or gasoline generator. The same advantage would apply to a fuel cell providing domestic electricity for a farm or other remote location, or powering a boat, an automobile, or any one of many such applications where electric motors can do the job.

The simplicity of the fuel cell leads to some unexpected advantages. We mentioned that there is no need for lubrication as required on turbines, diesel, and gasoline engines. Besides the saving in maintenance time, there is also a saving in precious petroleum products that can better be used for something else than reducing friction.

Starting a fuel cell requires only the closing of a switch. Starting a conventional engine can be more difficult, and is sometimes downright frustrating, as users of two-cycle gasoline engines for lawnmowers and motorboats may agree. Suppose we need a power supply in a remote area, and one which will run for long periods of time. It would be necessary periodically to check a gasoline or diesel generator. Not so with the fuel cell; just start it and leave it. It will run as long as there is fuel in the tank. Where intermittent operation is needed, the advantage is even greater. To start a reciprocating engine without human muscle power we need a starting motor, plus batteries to operate that motor. In cold weather, our conventional generator might be hard, or even impossible, to start. In hot weather it might also refuse to run. The fuel cell, however, starts with complete simplicity and dependability.

Because the fuel cell is so simple in operation, it is inherently a long-lived piece of equipment with no parts to wear out, overheat, or break. As an example, the power plant for

Apollo, one of the most complicated fuel-cell systems yet built, has performed satisfactory for 2,000 hours at a stretch in the laboratory.

The fuel cell can be operated in a mine, or other closed area occupied by human workers, with no danger. In submarines, gasoline engines once so threatened the lives of sailors that skippers took to putting cages of white mice in the engine rooms. The fuel cell, which produces no harmful exhaust, can be used safely. In fact, a one-man fuel-cell submarine has been built and operated successfully. The United States Navy is interested in such power plants for full-size undersea craft.

A most promising application for the fuel cell is in spacecraft. Here again, there is a closed area in which the exhaust from conventional engines poses difficulties. We shall devote a later chapter to this special use of the fuel cell.

One of the points in favor of the diesel engine when it was introduced was that it could run on fuels not usable by the gasoline engine. Although it does not operate, as some enthusiasts proclaimed, on "anything from beer to soapsuds," the diesel does profit from its fuel flexibility. The fuel cell gives similar promise of using many fuels. Thus, otherwise unusable fuels may be put to good account to save petroleum. Grass clippings, leaves, and sawdust are among the unusual fuels suggested to power biochemical fuel cells.

Electrochemistry and the Fuel Cell

One of the many fuel-cell applications that have been investigated in detail is its use as a power supply for industries that require large amounts of electricity. The production of aluminum is an electrolytic process and so much electricity is required that it is considered a "raw material." A point of interest is that the electricity is used as direct current at low voltage, conditions that the fuel cell meets very well.

One survey shows that a successful natural-gas fuel cell would lower the cost of electricity for the aluminum industry so much that a 10 per cent reduction in the price of the finished product might be made. Such a saving is typical of those the fuel cell might make elsewhere in the electrochemical industries. Magnesium is produced electrolytically, and the fuel cell might save 7 per cent of costs here. Hydrogen peroxide, manganese, sodium chlorate, phosphoric acid, zinc, and chlorine are other electrochemical products, and savings in cost ranging from 4 per cent to 15 per cent are estimated for fuel-cell power over conventional electricity.

An even more direct use of the fuel cell in the electrochemical industry may be possible. One writer has stated that it would be ironic if the fuel cell were to prove more useful when operated primarily as a producer of material rather than a converter of material into electricity. Let's look into this idea, starting off with present fuel cells primarily producing electricity.

We have seen that one of the advantages of the hydrogen-oxygen fuel cell for use in space is its production of pure water as a by-product, or exhaust. Also useful is the by-product of a sodium-chlorine fuel cell suggested for submarines. As we might guess from the fuel and oxidant, this fuel cell delivers common salt as its exhaust. It is hard to conceive of a submariner being wildly enthusiastic over table salt, living as he does in an ocean of the stuff. However, salt is only one of many possible yields from fuel cells.

A methyl or ethyl alcohol fuel cell can produce such useful

Fuel-cell battery, 12 inches square, developed by Esso Research and Engineering Company

chemicals as formic acid or acetic acid, plus a small amount of electricity. Biochemical fuel cells might similarly be operated with a main goal of yielding desired products rather than electricity. It might even be feasible to operate the fuel cell "in reverse" by applying electricity to its electrodes from an outside source to effect desired electrolyte action to break down compounds into their constituents.

Electrochemical engineers in industry are already making use of improvements stemming from fuel-cell research. This technology exchange works both ways. Scientists in England have developed a technique of using a "pulsed" voltage rather than steady voltage in industrial electrochemical processes. The product formed at the electrodes depends on the characteristics of the pulsating voltage. NASA has sponsored work in this country on the electric pulsing of fuel cells in an adaptation of the British idea. The fuel cell's future is linked intimately with that of electrochemistry.

Disadvantages

On the credit side of the ledger the fuel cell obviously shines, but we must also mention the disadvantages of the new power plant. If there were *no* drawbacks, the fuel cell would already be in wide use all around the world. Not just in space and military and laboratory applications, but in our automobiles, aircraft, factories, and even our homes. Let's look at these shortcomings.

A recent portable fuel cell for the military is far lighter than the battery pack or generator it replaces. It is much simpler, safer, and more reliable. It also costs thirty-three dollars per kilowatt-hour for the electricity it produces. If we paid that price for our domestic electricity it would take an annual income of many thousands of dollars just to pay the utility bill!

The reason for the high price of electric power in this example lies in the fuel selected for its excellent weight, bulk, and other characteristics. The idea is to find how to use cheaper fuels, as Esso Research and Engineering Company is doing with its methanol-air fuel cell. Methanol is wood alcohol, and this liquid can be produced now for about thirteen cents a gallon. The fuel cell converts this fuel to electricity at a creditable 40 per cent efficiency. So far, so good. But the unit weighs about 30 pounds, and produces only 100 watts of power at 5 volts. One horsepower at this rate would weigh more than 200 pounds, and 5 volts is a low figure when we are accustomed to appliances operating on 110 volts.

A 3-kilowatt (about 4 horsepower) fuel cell for a golf cart weighs something over 500 pounds, with fuel tanks and fuel. A light aircraft engine of about 100 horsepower weighs only 186 pounds. Even with tanks and fuel the total is still only 378 pounds.

The hydrox fuel cell uses gaseous fuels and thus requires very large tanks for long operation. This means undesirable weight and bulk. An alternative would be to pressurize the tanks, but this not only adds additional weight and cost, but makes the fuel cell hazardous because of the possibility of explosion. It also makes refueling a complicated operation, as compared with refueling a gasoline engine.

Low power-density is another handicap of the fuel cell at today's stage of development. For its size and weight it yields only a moderate amount of power. Attempts to increase the power output by drawing more power decrease efficiency of conversion, wasting power as heat. Thus the problem is one of compromise. At a temperature of about 1800° F., the fuel cell begins to lose its efficiency advantage over the Carnot cycle engine.

The low voltage of the fuel cell poses problems, too. Each cell produces only a fraction of a volt, and to raise the voltage it is necessary to "stack" many cells in series, just as we string flashlight cells together to power a light bulb. The power is direct current, instead of the alternating current most home appliances are designed for. Of course low-voltage motors are practical, but it will take time and money to make the switch. The fact that most existing equipment calls for high-voltage alternating current is a strong factor against an early swing to fuel cells.

Summary

The fuel cell has some handicaps that take away somewhat from the strong points in its favor. We should remember, however, that large-scale research and development of the fuel cell began only following World War II. Conventional steam power plants have been in use for a much longer time.

Thermal efficiency of fuel cell

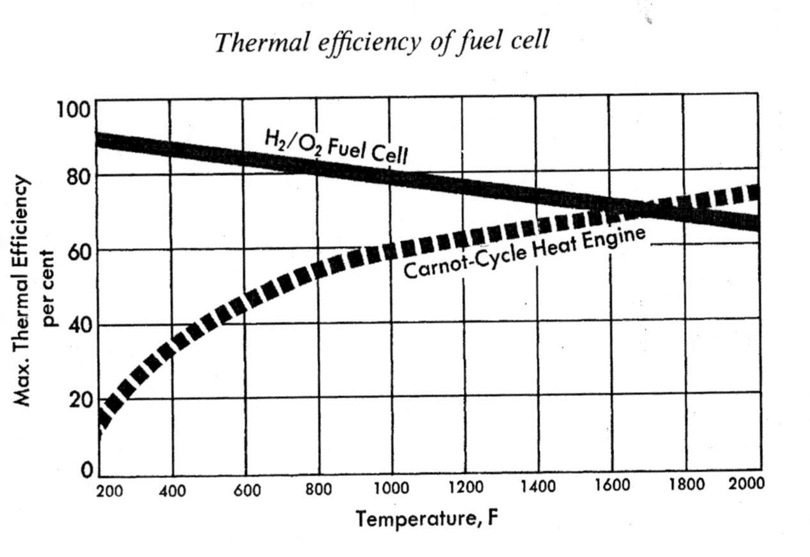

Steam engines and internal combustion engines are already as near to their ultimate efficiency and performance as they can be. The laws of thermodynamics set top practical limits to efficiency and thus we cannot hope for much more improvement of conventional engines.

But the fuel cell is still in its infancy, and the accelerated attack on the problems, commanding the attention of many of our best engineers and scientists, plus millions of dollars in private and government funds, seems sure to be successful.

So confident are proponents of the fuel cell of its ultimate victory in the power field that they have worked out detailed proposals for a number of applications that will compete with or replace conventional power sources. In the following chapters we shall look into some of these, including transportation, industry, and domestic uses.

CHAPTER FIVE

The Fuel Cell Grows Up

BASICALLY, the fuel cell is hardly any more complicated a power plant than a simple battery, as we have seen in the preceding chapters. However, there are a number of variations on the standard theme that make it a most interesting device. For example, Monsanto Chemical Corporation has developed what it calls a "dry tape" battery, a fuel cell in which the fuel is not a gas as in the hydrox cell, or a liquid as in the methanol-air cell, but a roll of tape. It is a very special tape, however, consisting of three layers: fuel, electrolyte, and oxidant. When passed between rollers the tape is crushed to release fuel and oxidant so that they contact the electrolyte and produce current flow.

There are even simpler versions of the fuel cell. One is called the "dissolved fuel" type. In the usual fuel cell, such as the hydrox, the electrolyte is contained in a sealed space between two electrodes. Fuel and oxygen are pumped to the other faces of these electrodes, and usually these spaces are sealed too. The fuel and oxidant diffuse through the porous electrodes to react with the electrolyte. But in the "dissolved fuel" cell the two electrodes are immersed in an unsealed container of electrolyte, which also contains the fuel, and the oxidant is drawn from the air. Very promising methanol-air fuel cells have been operated on this principle, and in a later chapter we shall see how to build our own demonstration fuel cell of this type for only a few dollars.

High-temperature Fuel Cells

The basic hydrox cell operates at room temperature or slightly higher, and at normal atmospheric pressure. Cheap hydrocarbon fuels like gasoline, kerosene, or natural gas will not react electrochemically under these conditions. To make these hydrocarbons "burn," the fuel cell must be heated to

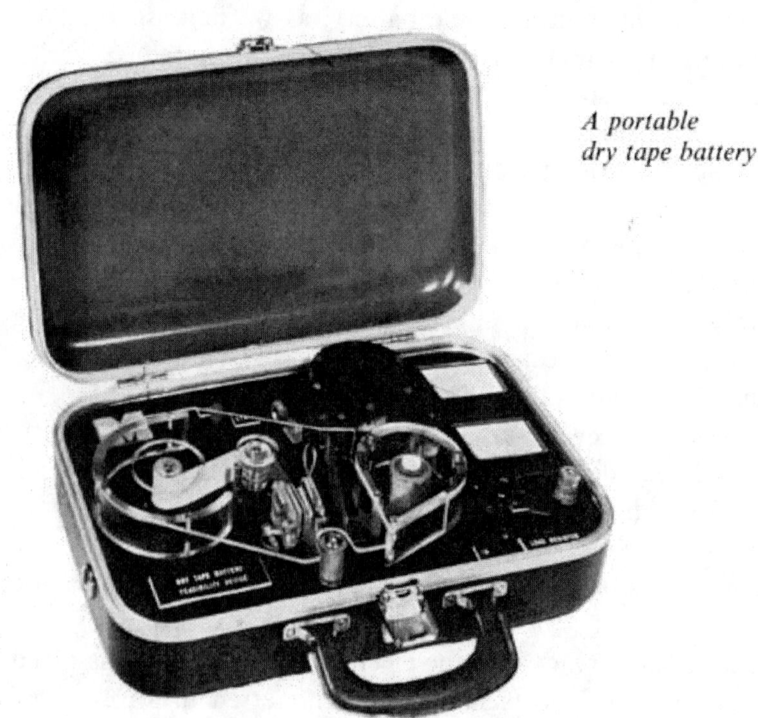

A portable dry tape battery

high temperatures. Sometimes the pressure is increased as well. The Bacon cell operates at somewhat higher temperature and pressure than most hydrox cells, but for the cheaper fuels, greatly elevated temperature is a must, and some fuel cells now under development operate at 1500° C. and higher. There are drawbacks to the high-temperature cell. Remember that the higher the temperature the lower the efficiency. But designers have the choice of low efficiency at high temperature, or no efficiency at lower temperatures.

We have seen that it is possible to crack or reform gasoline in a small apparatus attached to the fuel cell. The resulting hydrogen gas is then used in a more or less standard

Schematic drawing of a dry tape battery

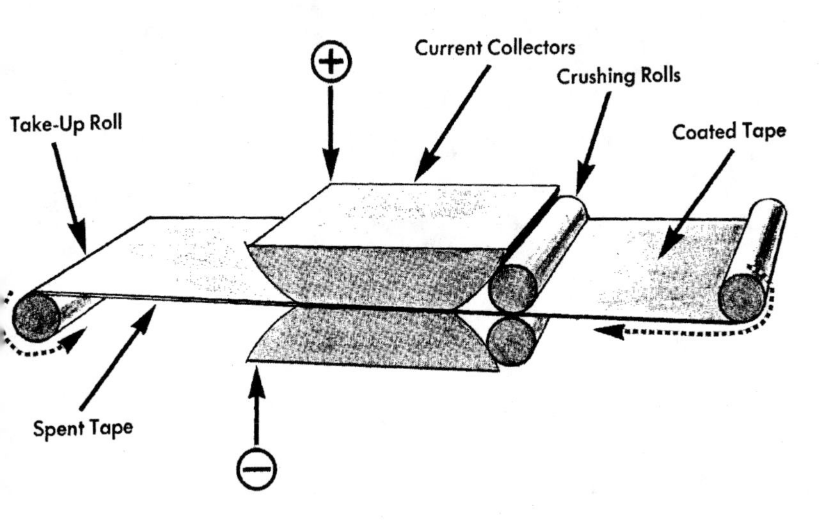

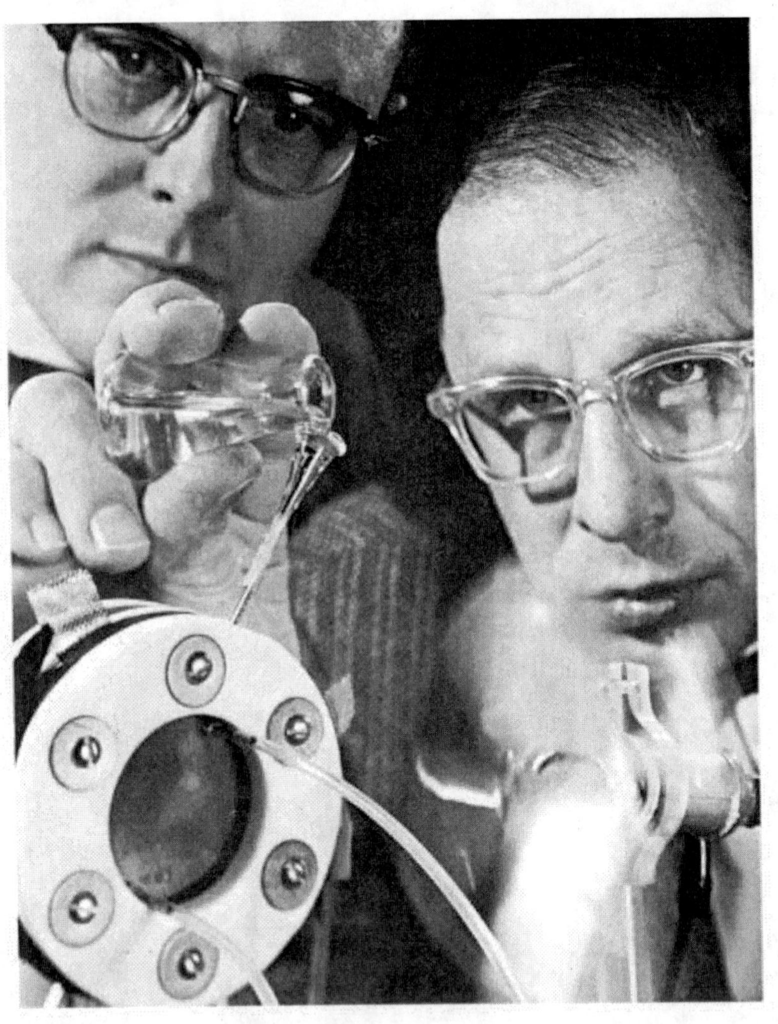

Inexpensive diesel oil combines with air in fuel cell to power motor.

hydrox cell. Of course, the addition of the reforming equipment adds cost, weight, and bulk to the once simple fuel cell and is a compromise to achieve low operating cost.

Another variation is the redox cell, so named for the reduction-oxidation process that takes place in it. Sir Eric Rideal, of whom we heard in Chapter 2, did much work with

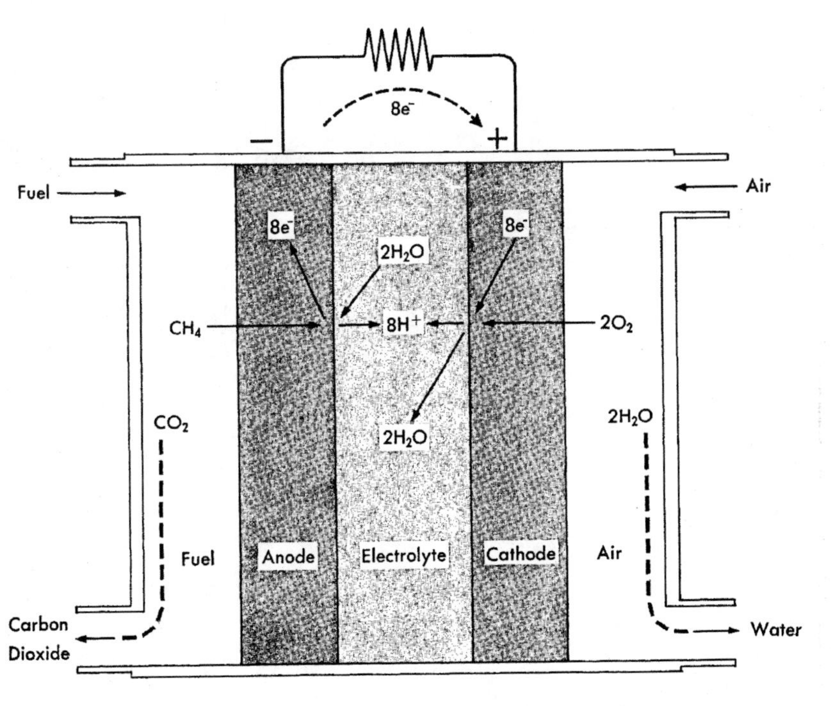

Diagram of fuel cell reactions, with methane as fuel

a redox fuel cell. We have seen that oxidation takes electrons away from the fuel. Reduction is the reverse process in which electrons are added to an electrode. The redox cell is actually an indirect fuel cell, as we can see by studying the operation of a typical example. This uses tin salts and bromine as "intermediates." When fuel in the form of hydrogen is provided

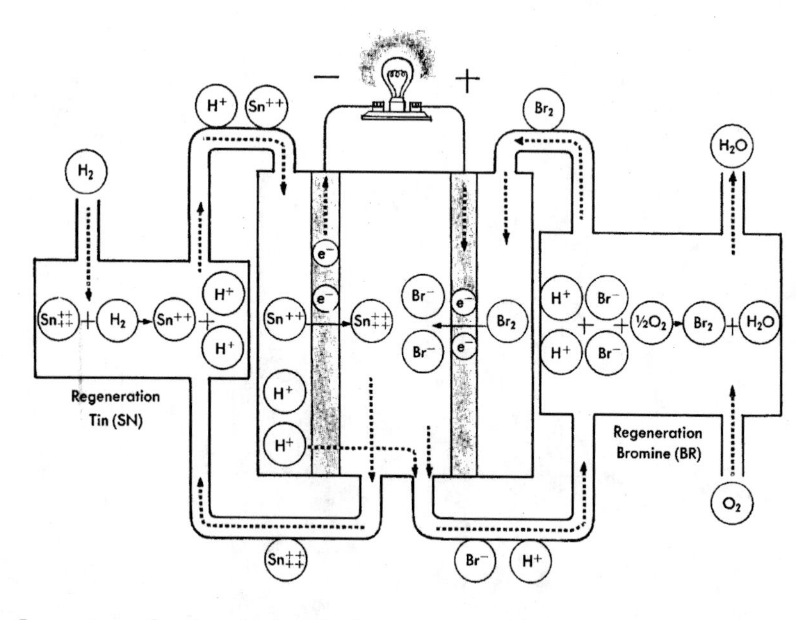

Operation of redox fuel cell, showing regenerators for tin and bromin

to the tin salts, reduction takes place and electrons are added to the tin. Next these electrons are given up to the negative electrode and pass through the external circuit while the tin returns to the fuel intake to receive more electrons. At the positive electrode, bromine takes the electrons from the electrode and carries them to the oxygen which removes them. More recently, General Electric Company has experimented with a redox cell using titanium rather than tin.

During this reduction-oxidation process the fuel and oxidant are constantly "regenerating" the intermediates.

There is another kind of regenerative fuel cell, in which the same "fuel" is used over and over, with energy being replaced in it at each cycle. There are several ways of regenerating the fuel, including thermal, electrolytic, and photolytic regeneration. We shall consider thermal regeneration first, since it is the simplest.

"Regenerative" Fuel Cells

Most engines operate on heat. In a steam engine, a heat source causes a thermochemical reaction, changing water to steam. The steam is then used to produce thermomechanical force. Heat engines are notoriously inefficient at the temperatures that are practical with commonly available materials, but heat can be changed into something other than mechanical energy.

In a thermochemical reaction a heat source adds energy to a chemical substance. Properly chosen, this substance can be made to give up its heat as electricity. Here, basically, is the principle of the regenerative fuel cell. It is attractive mainly as a way of obtaining cheap energy for the fuel cell. Someday we may burn coal directly in a fuel cell to provide a very cheap source of energy. Indirectly, through thermal regeneration, we can do it right now.

Just as hydrogen and oxygen combine in the fuel cell to produce water and electricity, other materials including metals produce the same reaction. Some fuel cells, like the lithium-hydrogen type, use one metal. There are also two-metal systems that use potassium and mercury. After the desired electrochemical reaction has taken place in the fuel cell, the solution is circulated by pumps to a boiler. Here heat is supplied from any external source and separation of the two components takes place. This thermomechanical separation regenerates the fuel so that it is capable of again combining and producing electricity.

The Allison Division of General Motors Corporation has operated a liquid-metal fuel cell, and points to the great power-to-weight advantage such a device has over a storage battery. While a storage battery about one cubic foot in volume yields only about 1500 watts, a liquid fuel cell the same size would deliver about 11,000 watts, more than seven times the power.

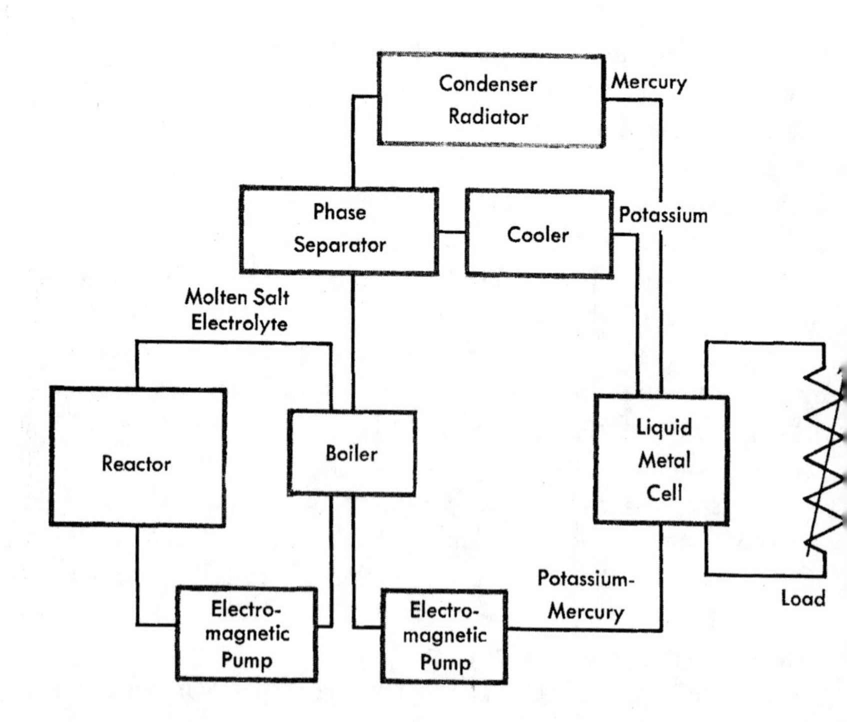

Diagram of a thermally regenerative fuel cell

Using a molten salt electrolyte, and operating at high temperature and pressure, the liquid-metal fuel cell boasts a much more rapid conversion of chemical energy into electrical energy to provide power. In a regenerative system it could be used with the heat supplied by a nuclear reactor. Allison has run its liquid-metal fuel cell for continuous periods of longer than 100 hours.

Whenever the word *thermomechanical* enters the picture we must be prepared to take the loss in efficiency dictated by the laws of thermodynamics. A fuel cell working with a regenerative system cannot show efficiencies in the 75 per cent range. Its efficiency will drop drastically due to the inevitable energy loss entailed in the separation of the solution into its two components because this separation is essentially a heat-engine process.

However, the regenerative fuel cell is still worth while from the standpoint of over-all efficiency and economy. We have substituted *heat* for expensive fuel. This heat can be furnished by coal, petroleum, or even nuclear reactors, which promise to be very cheap producers of power. While the regenerative fuel-cell system might not have an over-all efficiency greater than a conventional steam-turbine power plant, it can be much smaller and still produce electricity economically.

There is another source of heat available for use in the regenerative fuel-cell system. This is solar energy, and it will perhaps first be put to use in a space power plant.

Nuclear energy is an excellent source of power, but for some applications it has disadvantages too. Long ago a nuclear airplane was proposed and much money and time were expended on its design. However, there is no such aircraft yet flying, and it begins to look as though there may never be one. A nuclear reactor must be heavily shielded to safeguard the crew from dangerous radioactivity. In designing a ship, this is not too difficult a problem because weight is relatively unimportant. However, with aircraft—or spacecraft—weight is a great factor.

We have a few nuclear-powered spacecraft in operation at present. We have many more powered by solar energy. Thus far only solar batteries are in use in spacecraft. However, NASA and the United States Air Force have large solar "dynamic" power plants under development that will produce up to about 20 horsepower. Solar-fired steam engines are proposed for space and there are also solar-dynamic engines that use liquid metal or metal-hydride working mediums. If we can convert solar energy to electricity in this mechanical fashion, why not do it directly with a liquid-metal fuel cell?

Over long periods of time even the fuel cell requires an appreciable weight of fuel. For the weeks, months, or perhaps years required for interplanetary flights, fuel weight must be considered. The advantage of a "weightless" fuel grows with each hour to be spent in space where there are no filling stations or power plugs. Solar energy is a weightless fuel.

In continuous sunlight there might be no advantage in using a regenerative fuel-cell system. Solar batteries can do the job even more simply than the fuel cell. But for orbital flight wherein the craft is shadowed for part of each circuit about the earth, the fuel cell can store up energy from the sun for conversion to power during dark periods. Fuel weight will be only that of sufficient working medium for the fuel cell,

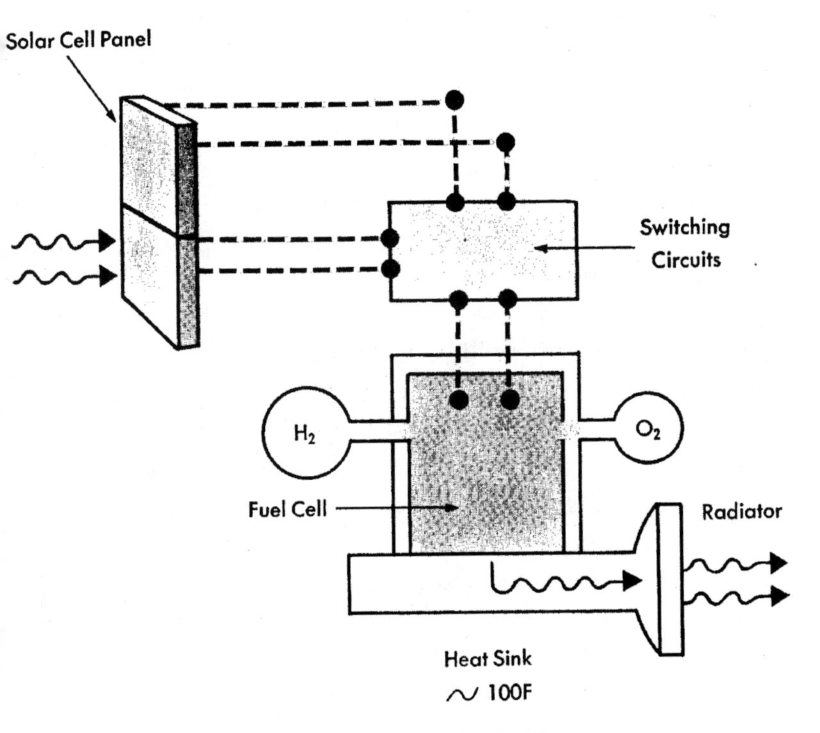

Solar-regenerative fuel cell

whether it operates an hour or a century—perhaps the closest thing to perpetual motion that man will ever achieve.

To furnish the heat for regenerating the fuel, a large collector or focusing mirror is needed to concentrate the sunlight on the boiler that separates the constituents of the fuel. This collector must be kept pointed at the sun for efficient operation. At first thought, such a system seems unwieldy and perhaps difficult or impossible to get into orbit. The

United States Air Force's 20-horsepower solar engine requires a 45-foot parabolic collecting mirror. However, such structures can be folded for launching, and opened after reaching orbit. Or they can be made of inflatable plastic. Since they are weightless in space, there is no problem of distortion and the lack of air (wind) makes a large, light structure feasible. Orienting them will require little power; perhaps the pressure of sunlight itself may be enough to keep them facing the sun.

Will there be any use for a solar-regenerated fuel cell on earth? Possibly there will. One of the disadvantages of using solar energy is that it is intermittent. When the sun goes down, solar power ceases, just when it is most needed for lighting, cooking, heating, and so on. What is needed is a means of storing the solar energy for later use.

Clever engineers have adopted such simple schemes as using a solar-powered motor to pump water up to a storage tank during the day, and letting the falling water drive a motor for nighttime use. This same system is used by power utilities for storing the output of its generators for use during peak hours of demand.

Suppose we decide on a 35,000-kilowatt power plant to supply a small town (an average home uses about 3 kilowatts of power). Further, we want to use solar energy to provide this power. We do not want power only when the sun shines, but will use a regenerative fuel-cell system to provide power on a twenty-four-hour basis. The sun shines only about one third of the time, so we design a solar power plant capable of producing 100,000 kilowatts during the daylight hours. We know that our over-all efficiency will not be 75 per cent, so let's take a more realistic figure like 5 per cent. What size solar installation will that require? It will be about one mile square, a rather huge power plant, compared with a steam-electric installation. But the solar heat collector might consist only of a body of water, a "solar pond" of the type researchers are now experimenting with. Salt added to the water creates denser layers toward the bottom, to prevent convection currents and retain much of the solar heat falling on the water. The solar pond will thus provide hot water to operate low-temperature turbines that produce electrical power. This will be fed to regenerative fuel cells.

In addition to electricity, the solar pond will have a couple of fairly useful by-products. If we are using sea water we can separate it into fresh water for drinking, and salt that can be sold as a commodity.

Thus far we have been talking about two ways of regenerating a fuel cell. We either pump electricity into it, as with a storage battery, or we use an electrochemical or thermomechanical reaction for separating the fuel that has combined in the cell. We can use electricity to electrolyze water and make hydrogen and oxygen, for example. We may also some day accomplish the *photolysis* of water. As the name of this phenomenon implies, this means dissociating, or separating, hydrogen and oxygen by means of light. This has been done on a very small scale, at low efficiency; ultraviolet light shining on water has broken water into hydrogen and oxygen.

Water is not the only compound that can be broken down by photolysis. Hydrogen peroxide also can be dissociated by light (this is why it is always kept in dark bottles) and so can nitrosyl chloride. The latter seems especially promising and much work using solar energy has been done, particularly at Stanford Research Institute. The result of this photochemical reaction is the production of nitric acid and chlorine, both of them useful as fuels, or recombinable to produce electricity.

More exotic methods have been proposed for using solar energy in fuel cells. Water can be recovered from the atmosphere by using absorption towers to trap moisture which is then evaporated by heating with focused sunlight. The reclaimed water could be electrolyzed or photolyzed to produce hydrogen and oxygen. Or the hydrogen could be combined with carbon dioxide (also recovered from the atmosphere by solar energy) to produce the liquid fuel methanol, already being used with air in fuel cells. Nitrogen, also taken from the atmosphere, combines with hydrogen to produce ammonia. This can be further changed chemically to nitric acid, which with the chlorine mentioned earlier might be used in a fuel cell.

While the basic fuel cell is a very simple device, there are many factors that lead to modifications of the original concept. Some of these changes are so drastic that the fuel cell is hardly recognizable. In the future even greater changes may take place to make a power producer that will be different from even the most sophisticated designs of today. However, the basic principle will remain just what it was in the days of Sir William Grove: the electrochemical production of electricity from fuel without changing the fuel cell itself.

CHAPTER SIX

Living Battery—The Biochemical Fuel Cell

IN THE PRECEDING CHAPTERS we have considered a number of fuel cells, and noted many improvements on early attempts at direct conversion of fuel into electricity. But consider the following statement by fuel-cell authority Will Mitchell, Jr.:

> "Perhaps the most highly refined fuel cell system today is the human body, a mechanism that catalytically (enzymes) burns (oxidizes) food (fuel) in an electrolyte (blood), to produce energy, some of which is electrical."

The designers of fuel cells, then, have merely been copying a model that nature has operated for countless years. Some of the power our bodies make from their fuel is electrical in nature. Nerve signals include minute electric currents, and our brains have been called "living computers" that operate partly on electrical power. Man has no monopoly on the production of living electricity. Fish, particularly, produce great amounts of electricity, and in the early days of science they were often used in the laboratory as living batteries. The electrophorus is a fish whose name is the same as that of a static electricity machine. Living things can properly be classed as "bioelectrochemical fuel cells," or biocells for short.

Although we make use of the electrical signals in our bodies for a number of purposes, no one has yet suggested connecting humans in a series-parallel combination to produce electricity. However, fuel-cell researchers have done just that with lesser living things. One result is the so-called "bug battery" which made news about 1960. In this living fuel cell, tiny organisms produced small amounts of electricity at an efficient conversion rate. Such biocells have been utilized in a variety of experiments.

In the chapter on the history of the fuel cell we saw that an English scientist in 1911 put together what was perhaps the first "artificial" biocell. This consisted of platinum electrodes, a fuel in the form of yeast, an oxidant, catalysts, and electrolytes, separated by a semipermeable membrane. Basically it was similar to the Grove hydrogen-oxygen cell that preceded it; man had at last discovered in nature the device he thought he had invented.

Potter connected six of his yeast cells in series and measured a current of 1.25 milliamperes in the external circuit that connected the fuel electrode and oxygen electrode. He knew exactly what he had achieved, and wrote in a descriptive paper, "The disintegration of organic compounds by microorganisms is accompanied by liberation of electrical energy."

The remarkable demonstration made little impression. Bacteria could produce a tiny current of electricity, and that was that. Not until 1930 would the feat be duplicated, this time by an American who put together a bio-battery similar to Potter's, and corroborated his results.

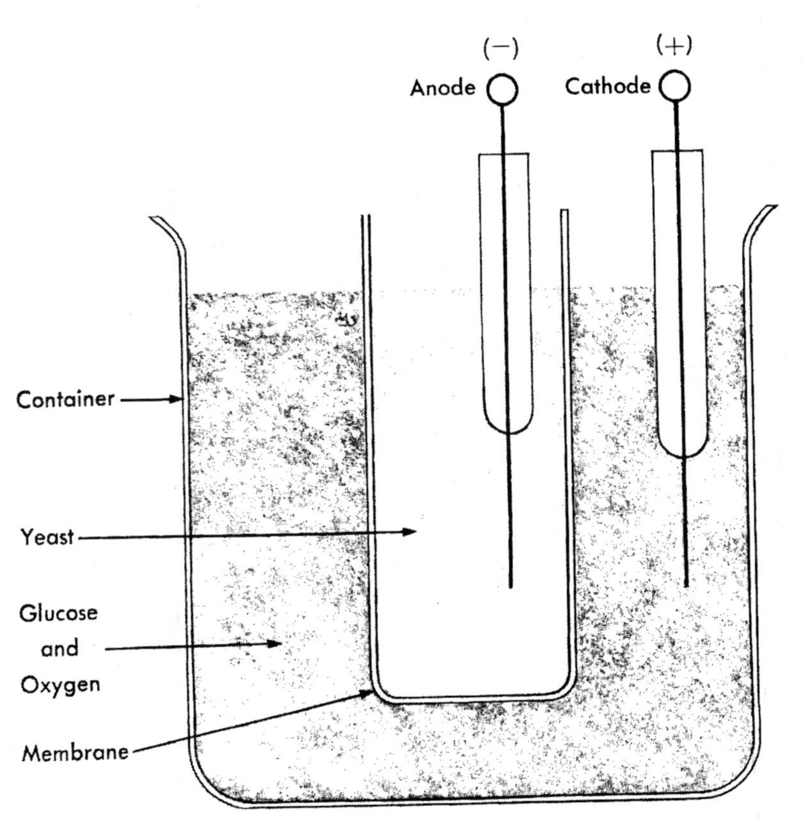

Potter's biocell

Dr. Barnett Cohen assembled a number of cells, each composed of ten cubic centimeters of a culture coupled with a sterile control cell. The bacterial culture also contained a "poising" agent such as potassium ferricyanide or benzoquinine. Each of these individual cells produced 0.2 milliampere of current at 0.5 volt. Cohen connected a large number of these to produce what he called a bacterial battery producing 2 milliamperes at 35 volts.

This seems a feeble amount of power to be produced with so much effort in the laboratory. It would have been sufficient to power a small transistorized radio—except that the transistor was not invented for another eighteen years. After demonstrating that his bacterial battery could generate appreciable amounts of electricity, Cohen apparently dropped his research in this direction.

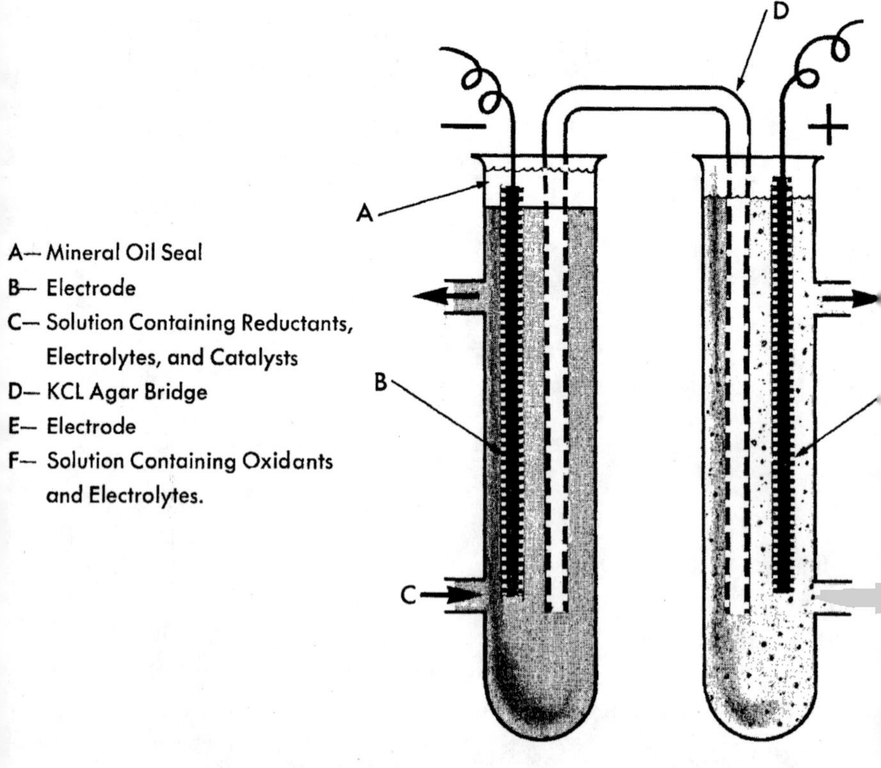

Biochemical fuel cell. The prototype unit shown was developed by research workers of the U. S. Geological Survey.

Two decades had elapsed between the first and second biocell demonstrations. Three more would go by before practical use was made of nature's fuel cell. In the late 1950's Bacon and others were making known their practical successes with "conventional" fuel cells. It was during this period that the biocell came alive again, in three separate projects.

John Welsh and Joseph Kaye headed a Cambridge, Massachusetts, research firm interested in direct conversion of fuel to electricity. The problem of catalysts prompted them to investigate the "enzymes" or living catalysts that promote energy exchange. Dr. Frederick Sisler, a biologist with the Department of the Interior's Geological Survey, was concerned with the decomposition of organic matter on the ocean bottom, and it occurred to him that here was an environment in the sea with conditions that would produce electric current. Magna Industries, Incorporated, in California, also got into the biocell field in a roundabout way. They were investigating the corrosion of undersea oil wells and pipe lines, and found that one cause of the destruction was electricity produced by marine bacteria.

Dr. Sisler was first to demonstrate publicly a fuel cell in which marine organisms acted as catalysts and stripped electrons from the fuel fed to them.

This marine biocell consisted of a test tube about 7 inches high and ¾ inch in diameter. The electrolyte was a "salt bridge" that permitted passage of ions, but prevented flow of other material that might be harmful to the isolated bacterial cultures. The bacteria fed on organic matter from the ocean, and converted part of the energy into free electrons that flowed, as in a conventional fuel cell, through an ex-

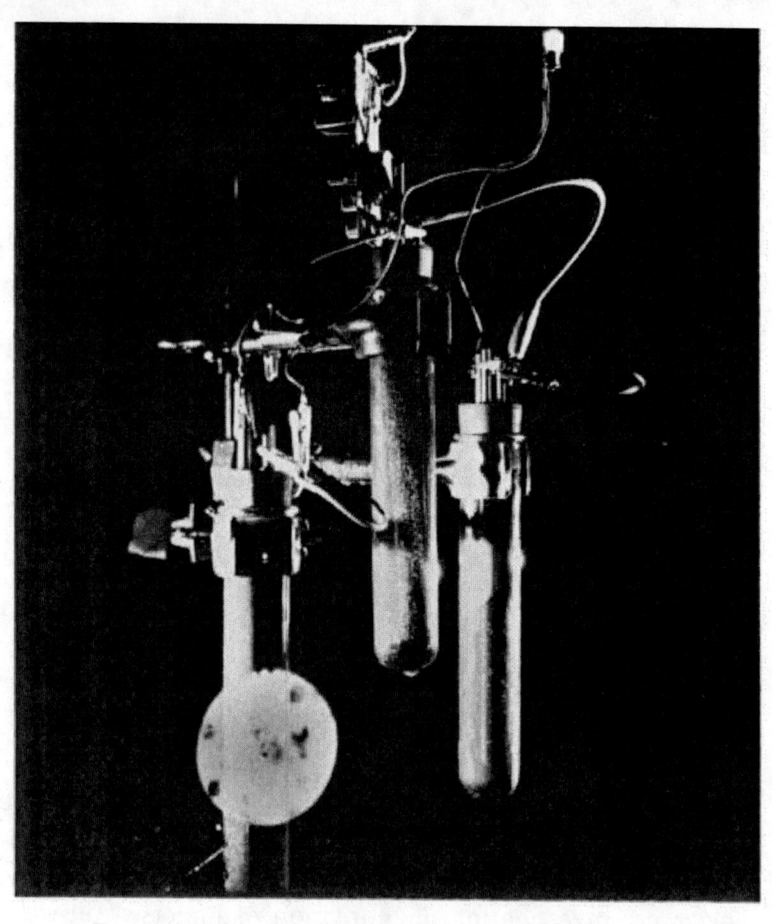

Battery powered by bacteria lights a bulb (top, right) and runs a small radio (top, center).

ternal circuit. Sisler demonstrated that his marine biocell could light a small electric lamp and also power a radio transmitter with a range of fifteen miles. Later improvements included the addition of bacteria on the electrodes to hasten the reaction rate. These more efficient fuel cells were demonstrated by Sisler in a small model boat propelled by the water it floated in!

While the biochemical fuel cell operated at atmospheric temperature and pressure, and was simpler in this respect

Sarbacher (left) and Sisler watch as bacteria-powered model boat moves through tank of sea water in their laboratory.

than the pressurized and heated artificial fuel cells, the nature of the new device made it basically more complicated. Rather than a single electrolyte fluid, some biocells required two different fluids. One, called the catholyte, was used in the cathode side of the cell. The other was called the anolyte and was necessary to carry out the required reactions at the anode. These separate electrolytes were contained in different beakers joined by the salt bridge for ion flow, or used a semipermeable membrane such as cellophane, that allows the desired ion flow but is impervious to larger particles that might adversely affect the operation of the cell.

Magna Industries built marine biocells for the United States Navy, capable of generating small amounts of power for radio transmitters in marker buoys and other such equipment. Other firms marketed inexpensive bacterial fuel cells suitable for laboratory demonstrations and science fairs. These bio-batteries were powerful enough to operate small radios, motors, and so on.

Advantages of the Biocell

Because the biocell consists of living organisms, the conversion of fuel to electricity takes place at about the ambient, or surrounding, temperature and pressure. It also takes place in a neutral liquid medium, in which living catalysts promote the desired reaction. A further convenience is the fact that the "fuel" burned in the biocell may be material of no use for anything else: sea water, for example, or dried corn husks, sewage, grass cuttings, or sawdust. All these materials can be fed to hungry bacteria and turned into electricity in the process. The United States Bureau of Mines demonstrated an experimental biocell fueled with iron pyrites, or fool's gold. Algae can be used to convert sunlight into electricity, functioning as a living solar battery.

With the introduction of Sisler's biocell and announcement of success by other researchers, optimism was great for the new "living" fuel cell. In 1960 a scientist predicted that it might one day be possible to produce one watt of power in a bacterial cell. Almost as soon as the prediction was made it became an accomplished fact. The United States Navy contracted for marine biocells. As we have seen, the Bureau

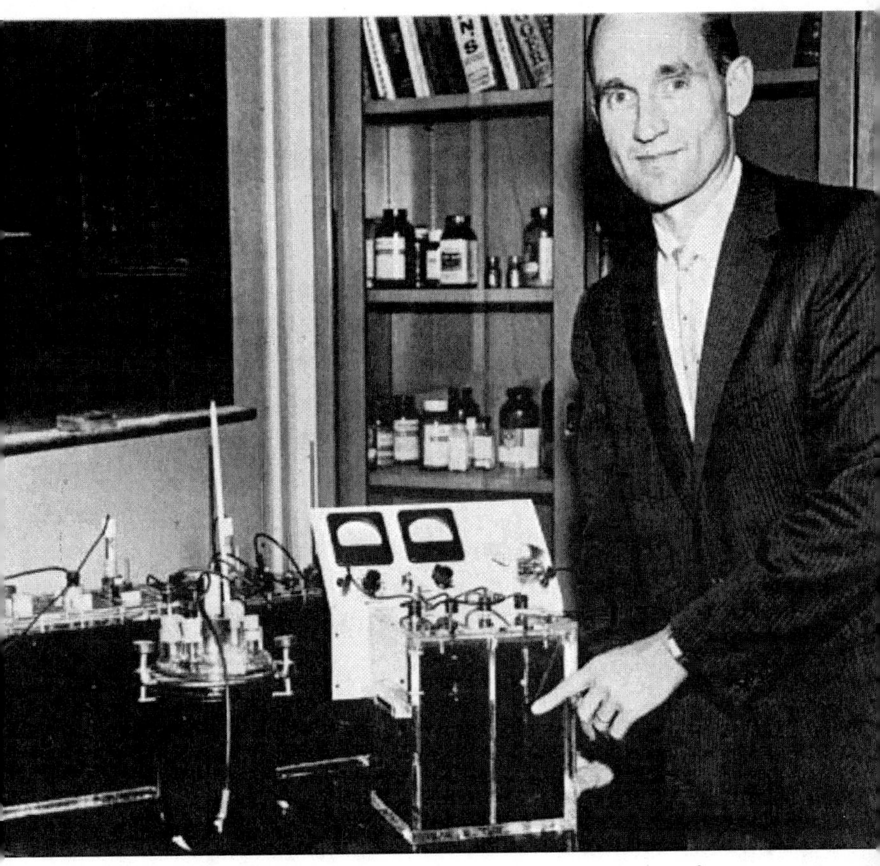

Dr. Rohnback, head of Magna Industries, Incorporated, shows an experimental marine biocell.

of Mines did research work, thinking of the fuel cell both as a safe source of electric power for lighting mines and working small equipment, and also as a device for bioelectrochemical separation of minerals from solution. The United States Army also encouraged biocell research, interested in the idea of portable power units that might be fueled with vegetation or even useless wastes. NASA sponsored a number of separate research programs to be carried out by the Philco Corporation, Melpar, Incorporated, and Magna Industries. For several years the biocell was the new wonder baby of the sciences.

There seemed to be a number of bacteria suitable for biocell work. Among the first were *Escherichia coli* and *Desulfibrio sulfuricans.* Potter and Cohen had long ago demonstrated that yeast cultures produced electricity. Now mushrooms were proved suitable. To "fuel" the bacteria there were such organic materials as glucose, urea, lactate, and formic acid. Work was done with bioanodes, biocathodes, or both.

Two types of bacterial energy conversion are available: aerobic and anaerobic. In the aerobic oxidation-reduction process, the reactions end with the acceptance of hydrogen by molecular oxygen; this is the case when aerobic or "air-breathing" bacteria are used as the biocells. In addition to energy, the aerobic process yields carbon dioxide and water.

In the anaerobic process, more commonly known as fermentation, there is no air to provide oxygen, as in the aerobic process. Complete oxidation cannot take place, and the byproducts are organic acids and alcohol. Hydrogen is accepted by sulfates, nitrates, or carbonates to provide electron flow.

There are disadvantages in a biocell, just as there are in any fuel cell. Part of the fuel is used up to keep the bacteria alive, and this lowers the maximum attainable efficiency. The power density of a biocell amounts to only a few amperes per square foot of electrode surface, far less than the conventional fuel cell, which itself is not a very compact producer of power.

Unscientific news releases predicted high-powered biocells in the near future. The oceans would be turned into giant T.V.A. projects, and grass cuttings and sewage would provide all the industrial and domestic electricity needed. Actually, however, the biocell was not yet ready to deliver any such rewards.

Even the promising marine biocells were found to lose their power rapidly when left in the ocean. Other types did not function long either, as the bacteria became poisoned by contaminating materials or produced electricity at so slow a rate as to be of no practical use. It became obvious that a practical biocell, although possible, was not going to be perfected overnight. All the problems of the conventional fuel cell were also encountered—those of power density, polarization, catalysts, and so on—and the resulting difficulties were

A marine biocell kit uses anaerobic bacteria, which reduce sulfate.

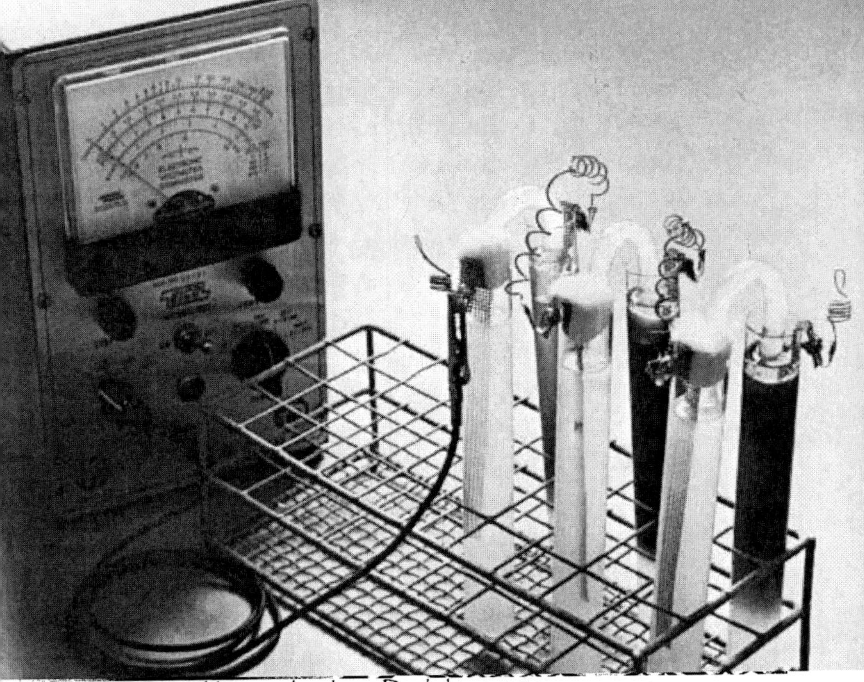

even compounded. A biochemical fuel cell could power a small radio or a light bulb, but it was not yet going to drive motors or radar sets.

Many researchers became disenchanted, but a few persevered. Some began to investigate the use of bacteria in hydrocarbon fuel cells. Others worked on the idea of converting cheap fuel such as sewage, grass cuttings, and other waste vegetation into more refined fuel for subsequent use in a fuel cell. We have seen the need for "reformers" to convert cheap fuel into something the conventional fuel cell can operate on. Here was a natural reforming system. At Melpar, Incorporated, researchers found that certain strains of bacteria were marvelously effective in converting waste into hydrogen gas. Here was a possible way of operating a hydrox fuel cell on cheap fuel.

Scientists now suggest that the biocell will find its place as an auxiliary device such as the hydrogen gas producer, or used as a part of a closed environmental system for spacecraft, reclaiming what would otherwise be waste or even noxious material. NASA agrees, and possibly some future space vehicle will be fitted with a biochemical fuel-cell system that produces small amounts of electricity as a by-product while it reclaims air and water.

Just as a small biocell might operate on wastes in space vehicles, a larger one might reclaim some electrical power from the sewage system of a city, or from the waste products of lumber and paper mills and other industrial projects.

Although about twenty years of accelerated work has been done on the inorganic fuel cell, the biocell has been under serious development only since 1960. The next fifteen years may see progress in this field comparable to that of the more

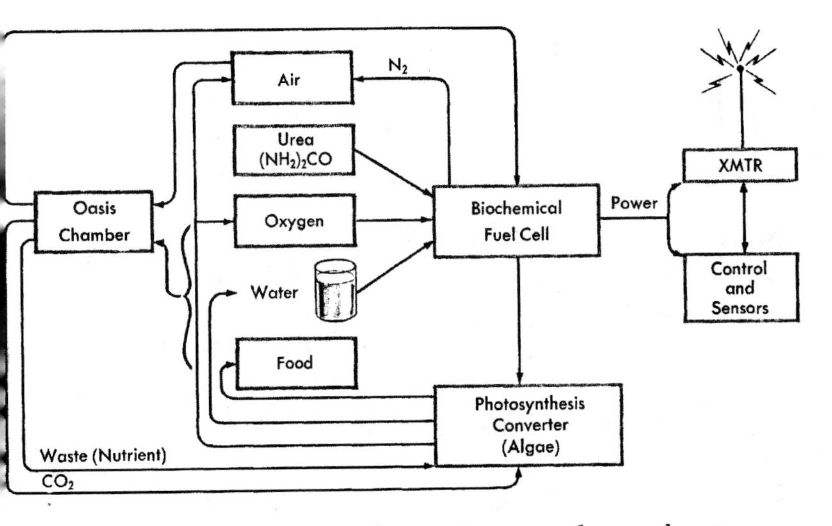

A "space oasis." Diagram of an environmental control system

conventional fuel cell. It may also see some mixtures of the two main ideas. Bacterial catalysts may be combined with cheap hydrocarbon fuel cells to produce the long-dreamed-of economical fuel-cell power plant. And, conversely, some inorganic technique may materially aid the bioelectrochemical fuel cell toward greater power density or some other desirable improvement.

CHAPTER SEVEN

Fuel Cells in Space

THE FIRST demonstrations of the fuel cell were in such terrestrial jobs as powering saws, spot welders, tractors, and golf carts. But the first practical application of the new power source came in space. On earth, conventionally powered tractors and golf carts were cheaper than the fuel-cell models; in space the power picture is quite different. Space satellites and vehicles boomed the revolutionary solar cell, and the same thing has happened with respect to the fuel cell.

Lifting a pound of equipment into orbit or beyond expends a very great amount of power; any saving in weight in heavy spacecraft is of vital interest. When the fuel cell began to demonstrate that it could provide electric power at a saving in weight over batteries—even the most advanced and expensive batteries—NASA officials turned eagerly to the fuel cell.

In 1958 our Vanguard satellite went into orbit. Its power supply consisted of a few storage batteries, and an array of solar cells with a total output of a few watts. The storage batteries soon went dead, but the solar cells continued to transmit for seven years. To provide even this small amount of power for seven years with storage batteries would have added hundreds of pounds of weight to the satellite, a sphere weighing only eleven pounds to begin with.

Today's spacecraft demand far more electrical power than did the tiny Vanguard and other unmanned craft. The need for one kilowatt—a thousand watts—of electricity is not out of the ordinary; Gemini and the three-man Apollo moon craft will require more than two kilowatts of power. This could be provided by solar cells, but would necessitate a huge solar panel accurately pointed at the sun. A more conventional power system was indicated for the present.

NASA's space-power goal is to obtain lightweight, dependable power sources for such uses as communications equipment; command and control; guidance; radar; image acquisition, processing, and transmission; data handling and storage; life support; experiments on planetary surfaces and environment; and for surface-exploration vehicles.

This sounds like a big order and it is. Most normal engineering problems are made far more difficult because of the space environment. Among such considerations, NASA lists the need for very high reliability, since chances for repair are extremely limited, and the need for high output of energy and power combined with light weight because of the very great cost of putting spacecraft aloft (a cost ranging from one thousand to five thousand dollars per pound). Other special problems are raised by the fact that gravity will vary during the course of a flight. It may be entirely absent during part of a space flight and higher than normal at other times. Also, extremes of heat and cold exist, as well as the hazards of vacuum, radiation, and meteoroids, so the ideal power system must not be affected by these factors.

Apollo fuel-cell power plant

Proof of NASA's faith in the fuel cell is reflected in the amount of money that we're willing to spend for the power systems for Gemini and Apollo—about fifty million dollars.

In the Mercury spacecraft and early Gemini missions in which our astronauts orbited the earth for durations up to several days, storage batteries provided power. These added many pounds of expensive weight; for Gemini and Apollo a better system was needed, one not requiring the use of a gasoline or diesel generator, as the exhaust from such a system posed problems. So did the generation of heat, vibration, and the radio "noise" of an ignition system that might confuse communications. The fuel cell has none of these drawbacks.

From a weight standpoint the fuel cell compared favorably with conventional internal-combustion generators. It was vibrationless and produced no harmful exhaust—in fact, the exhaust it did produce was one of the key reasons for considering it for space use. During evaluation tests for NASA, an engineer ran a hydrogen-oxygen fuel cell continuously for forty-eight hours. Then he dramatically filled a glass with the exhaust product from the power plant—and drank it. It was, of course, H_2O, or water. Here was a potentially great weight saving in the fuel cell. In a gasoline or diesel generator, the exhaust is poisonous and must be dumped overboard. All the fuel weight of the old-fashioned system is undesirable dead weight after combustion. Not so in the case of the fuel cell. Its fuel gases combine into water that can be used not only for cooling some of the equipment on board, but for drinking purposes.

A man requires about two quarts of water per day for health and comfort. Let us imagine a spacecraft like Apollo, carrying a crew of three, and with mission requirements including trips of fourteen days. A total of eighty-four quarts of water will be needed, and this amounts to roughly 160 pounds of weight. Add this to the weight of the storage batteries that would be needed over that two-week period, and you can see why the advantages of the weight-saving, water- and power-producing fuel cell shine brightly.

The new candidate for power looked excellent, but there were many questions to be answered before it would pass its space tests and be accepted. Fuel cells had performed well on the ground, but space is a completely different environment. NASA commissioned the Allis-Chalmers Manufacturing Company, whose fuel cells had powered tractors and golf carts, to build a pioneering space fuel cell that would

Personal check of fuel-cell water

prove whether or not the device could operate as well in orbit as on the ground.

It was the zero-gravity environment that gave most concern. The fuel-cell reaction is chemical and might depend in part on the force of gravity. Would the exchange of ions through the electrolyte solution take place efficiently; would fuel feed properly to the electrodes; and would the water byproduct be expelled if it was weightless?

In the fall of 1960, a General Electric fuel cell was loaded into the nose cone of an Atlas missile. Fired from Cape Canaveral, the nose cone sustained twenty minutes of weightless flight during its 600-mile-high trajectory. In addition to the zero-gravity condition, accelerations ranged as high as 50 gravities during the flight. Van Allen belt radiation was also sustained. Despite all these adverse conditions, the fuel cell performed constantly through the flight.

First test of the the Allis-Chalmers 50-watt pilot space fuel cell came not in an orbiting satellite, but aboard an Air Force KC-135 tanker aircraft. Just as astronauts were subjected to zero gravity in special flight maneuvers, the fuel cell was also made weightless as the tanker flew a certain path. And still it functioned perfectly. There were also vibration, shock, acceleration, and temperature tests. In each, a perfect score for the fuel cell. So into space it went for the final crucial test. It worked like a charm. This was in 1963.

To the General Electric Company went the job of building a fuel cell for the two-man Gemini spacecraft, and to United Aircraft's Pratt & Whitney Aircraft Division the task of building fuel cells for Apollo and also for Apollo's "Lunar Excursion Module" or LEM. This is the vehicle that will take astronauts from lunar orbit to a landing on the moon itself and then back to the Apollo.

The Gemini Fuel Cell

The fuel cell chosen by General Electric for the Gemini mission was a hydrogen-oxygen or hydrox type. However, it differed markedly from other fuel cells with respect to the electrolyte used. Instead of an aqueous type, GE substituted a *solid* electrolyte it had flight-tested in 1960. As we saw in Chapter 3, this new electrolyte passes ions through a membrane of semipermeable polystyrene plastic. Although the solid electrolyte does not yield as much power per volume as liquid electrolytes, it may result in greater reliability in a weightless environment. It also makes unnecessary the complex water-removal equipment of the aqueous electrolyte system. Cloth wicks carry off the water by capillary action, rather than gravity or pumping as done in other fuel-cell systems.

General Electric also chose to use a low-temperature, low-pressure fuel cell rather than the Bacon cell which operates at elevated temperature and pressure. The Gemini fuel cell operates in the range from 100° to 140° F. and at two atmospheres pressure, or less. Despite this, it develops as much as 2 kilowatts of power and operates at between 40 per cent and 60 per cent efficiency. It also produces about one pint of cooling and drinking water per kilowatt-hour of power.

The complete Gemini power plant consists of two fuel cells, each made up of three stacks of thirty-two individual cells. The system includes a preheater for the oxygen, a pump and radiator for the liquid coolant which carries off the small amount of heat the fuel cells generate, and an accumulator for the exhaust water. There are also electrical controls and instruments for operation of the power plant. Each fuel cell is enclosed within a metal "can" about one foot in diameter and three feet long, and weighs about 145 pounds.

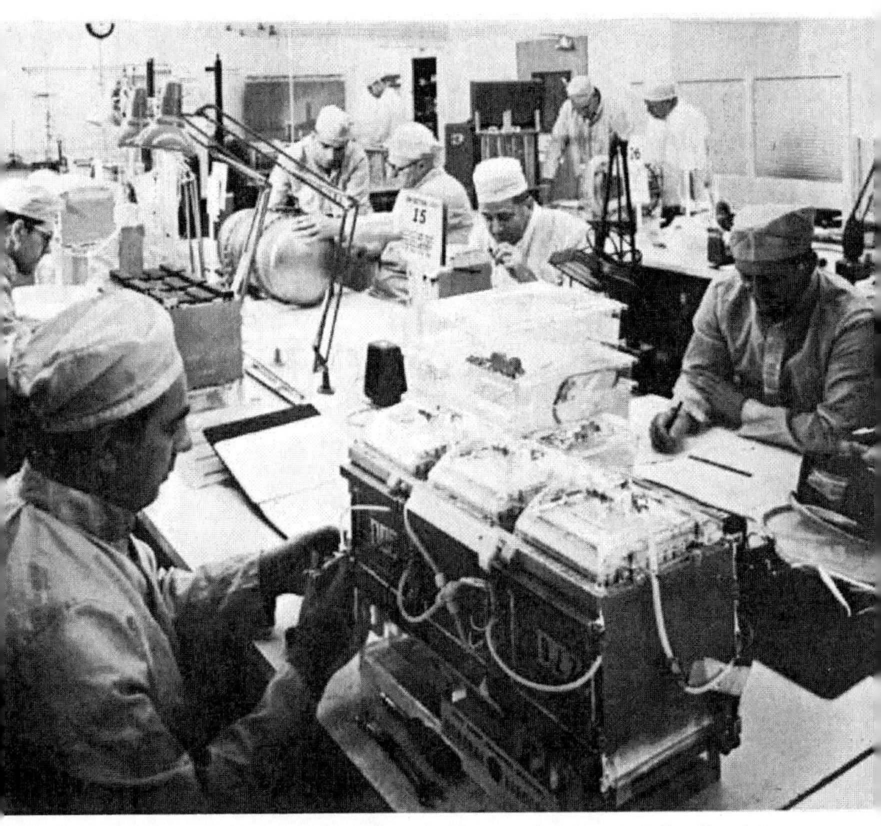

ssembling fuel cell "stacks" (modules) into "sections" (batteries) for Gemini

Gemini's longest mission requirement is fourteen days, and the fuel cell has been operated for more than two thousand hours, far longer than will be required in the space missions.

The decision to use fuel cells in spacecraft came too late for scheduling them in early Gemini missions. The unmanned flights, and manned flights through the four-day mission in June 1965, were made with conventional storage batteries. However, fuel-cell power was used in the subsequent missions.

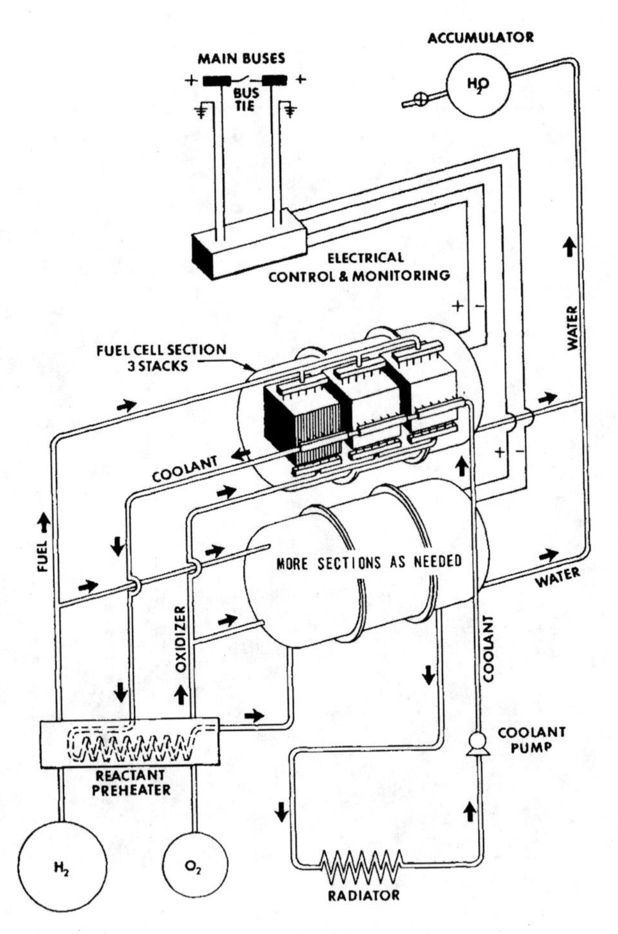

Gemini fuel battery

On August 21, 1965, the fuel cell got its first real trial aboard Gemini 5, which carried astronauts Cooper and Conrad into orbit. Early in the flight it appeared that the fuel cell—and the entire nine-day mission along with it—was doomed to failure. Pressure in the oxygen lines dropped drastically, and power decreased. A heater designed to warm up the liquid oxygen malfunctioned and the fuel cell was unable to deliver full power.

The planned rendezvous attempt was dropped, but as the hours passed, the fuel cell slowly increased its power until it was obvious that the entire mission could be flown. Later a NASA spokesman, far from finding fault with the fuel cell, said, "This seems to be a device that can take quite a beating." He pointed out that it was not the fuel cell, but auxiliary equipment that had caused the trouble. Steps were taken to guard against a recurrence of the problem. As a safeguard, fresh water had been carried along on the Gemini 5 mission, and also was used on the fourteen-day Gemini 7 flight.

The historic flights of Gemini 6 and Gemini 7, including the rendezvous of the two spacecraft, firmly established the fuel cell as a space power supply. With only minor troubles the fuel cells aboard both craft performed well, and those on Gemini 7 proved they could function for two weeks.

Apollo

By 1970, according to the present timetable, the giant Apollo vehicle will blast off for the moon, with three astronauts aboard. Days later it will go into a "parking" orbit about the moon. The LEM (Lunar Excursion Module) will detach itself and carry two of the crew to the moon for an actual landing and an exploration trip of the surface. Then it will rocket from the moon back up to the waiting Apollo, and all three astronauts will return to earth. This fantastic undertaking, the dream of centuries come true at last, will require a great deal of electric power aboard both the Apollo and the LEM. That power will be provided by fuel cells.

In 1958, when Apollo was only a glimmer in the minds of space planners, engineer W. H. Podolny of Pratt & Whitney Aircraft became convinced that the fuel cell was an important new power source for the near future. He persuaded his company to go into development of the new device. In 1960 Pratt & Whitney acquired the patent rights to the famous Bacon cell, the high-temperature, high-pressure hydrox cell with which Bacon had generated up to several kilowatts of power in his English experiments.

Inventor Francis Bacon demonstrated a hydrox cell developing more than five kilowatts for Pratt & Whitney. This was a heavy, "boiler-plate" design to prove the ability of his fuel cell. Soon afterward, company engineers demonstrated a much smaller, but "cleaned-up" version for NASA. This was the unit which produced 250 watts, and also pure water as Podolny dramatically demonstrated by drinking a glass of it. NASA was convinced that here was the logical power plant for the Apollo program, then getting into full swing, and Pratt & Whitney was selected to build the fuel cells for the spacecraft.

The Apollo fuel cell differs from the Gemini power plant mainly in that it is the Bacon type, operating with liquid electrolyte and at high temperature and pressure. The Apollo fuel cell units weigh 190 pounds and are about the same size as those of Gemini. However, the Apollo design produces a maximum power of close to 2½ kilowatts, more than three horsepower. It operates at higher efficiency than the GE solid-electrolyte device, and yields one quart of water per kilowatt-hour rather than one pint.

For the LEM a smaller fuel cell was designed. The craft that will land on the moon does not have the power requirements of the mother ship, and its power plant will develop a peak power of only one kilowatt. It will not produce water, being an "open-cycle" type in which the waste water will be dumped overboard rather than used for cooling and drinking purposes. This results in a lighter and more compact unit, and the LEM fuel cell will be about one-third the size and weight of the one on its Apollo mother ship.

Early in 1963 Pratt & Whitney tested the first three Apollo fuel cells. The Apollo fuel cell, named the 3A, soon proved its reliability. Pratt & Whitney ran test models for long periods and by the spring of 1964 a complete 3A power

Apollo fuel-cell system

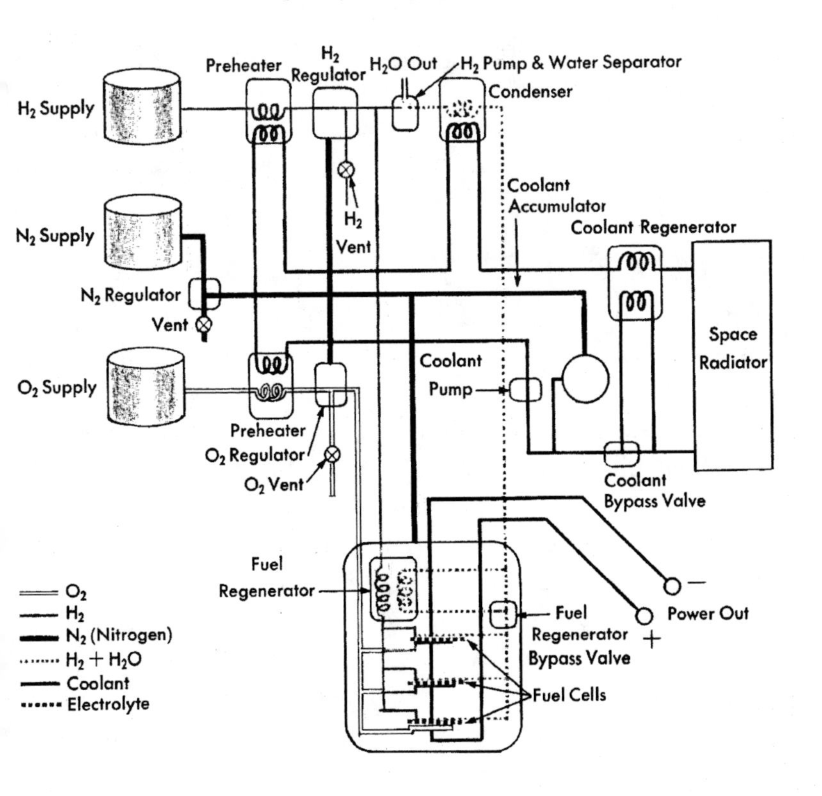

plant operated successfully for more than four hundred hours, longer than the scheduled fourteen-day mission of Apollo. Early in 1965, this was extended to one thousand hours, more than forty days.

Not only did the Apollo fuel-cell system meet all its requirements in spite of the accelerated development program, but its designers made the following optimistic predictions for future space fuel cells:

1. Power density of the fuel cell can be quadrupled, preserving the same high efficiency.
2. For the same power, the size and weight of the fuel cell can be cut in half.
3. The service life of the system can be 2,500 hours, and here the limiting factors will be mechanical parts such as pumps, and not the fuel cell itself.

Beyond Gemini and Apollo

For the fuel cell, Gemini and Apollo represent only proving grounds. NASA will also use the device aboard another spacecraft called Biosatellite, whose mission time is far longer than that of Gemini or Apollo. Another probability is a fuel-cell installation on the MOL, or Manned Orbital Laboratory, which will remain in space perhaps for years.

The Biosatellite fuel cell will consist of a stack of 32 cells producing about ⅓ kilowatt of power. It will weigh 35 pounds and use 0.8 pound of hydrogen and oxygen an hour, converting them to water in the process. This water will be useful in cooling equipment and then will be consumed by the animals aboard Biosatellite. Complete with fuel for a thirty-day mission, the fuel cell will weigh only 210 pounds. If NASA had to use storage batteries, the total weight would be about 800 pounds, plus the additional weight of water, since conventional batteries produce no such useful by-product.

An interesting idea of NASA planners is for fuel cells to operate on a variety of chemicals so that they could be fueled with rocket propellant, for example, rather than special fuel of their own. However, with duration and power requirements increasing rapidly, still a different kind of fuel cell may be called upon to save additional weight for spacecraft. This is the regenerative type (which we discussed in Chapter 5). As we have seen, by means of the simple fuel cell, we can extract the energy from fuel, and there is still the original weight left. The fuel, then, is not used up but is actually only a working medium. Could we somehow pump energy back into that fluid or gas, changing it back to reusable form? We can and we have.

In a steam engine it is possible to recirculate the condensed steam and boil this water again to make more steam. This is called thermal regeneration. In other words, heat continually added to the same working medium is available as power to drive the engine. Regeneration, particularly of liquid metals, is a good possibility for fuel cells in space. The next question, of course, is where the heat will come from. Two good sources come to mind: nuclear energy and solar energy.

The idea of using a radioisotope source or a small nuclear reactor to thermally regenerate space engines is not new; NASA has several such projects under way. There are steam engines, hot-air engines, and liquid-metal engines included in these strange power plants for space, with nuclear energy a candidate as a heat source for the regeneration process. Although the light weight of the nuclear fuel used to produce such heat is an advantage, this advantage is canceled out by the weight of the lead or other material that would have to be used to shield the resultant radiation. For that reason, another heat source may be more useful in space—regenerative fuel cells.

Solar dynamic engines in design and development stages for space are about as numerous as are nuclear types. Each square yard of area in deep space represents a potential of two horsepower, thus a solar collector area of just three square yards would provide sufficient energy to regenerate a fuel cell the size of the Apollo device, assuming 50 per cent efficiency of conversion.

In the hydrox cell we do not have quite as simple a problem as that of the steam engine operated as a closed-cycle regenerative system. Instead of boiling water we must break down the exhaust water from the fuel cell into hydrogen and oxygen, and feed it back to the electrodes in the fuel cell. The simplest way to do this is with electricity, and we might drive a turboelectric generator with solar energy and use its output to electrolyze the water, separating it into its original parts.

The advantages of such a regenerative fuel cell begin to be obvious when we consider manned orbiting laboratories permanently placed in space, or trips to the planets and beyond that will require months and even years. Any but nuclear fuel would be prohibitive in weight. But no matter how slight its own weight, nuclear fuel necessitates heavy shielding. Sunlight, on the other hand, is about the lightest thing we know of. Of course, the farther we travel from the sun the less energy reaches us in sunshine.

One indirect method of producing electricity from nature

is to burn methane gas, which is produced in sewage or other decaying matter. However, there is a more direct way of conversion of this gas: in a fuel cell. Thinking along these lines, NASA space planners sponsored research on biocells that operate on human waste as fuel. Waste material might fuel a battery to operate communications and control equipment, provide lights, and so on.

Welcome Fallout From Space

As often happens, research and development for a particular task result in benefits for completely different fields. It is easy to exclaim worriedly over the expenditure of millions of dollars for fuel cells for Gemini and Apollo—until we consider what the application of fuel cells on earth can mean.

General Electric suggests that we may well pull the fuel cell down from the sky by using cheaper hydrocarbon fuel. For a starter, they suggest powering the remote tracking stations used in our space program with fuel cells rather than conventional electric generators. This is still a special kind of power need, and the hydrocarbon fuel cell of today is not competitive with the electricity we draw from domestic wall sockets. But at least it gets us down to earth.

Pratt & Whitney too has already made steps in the direction of applications that are a far cry from space vehicles. In the same year that the firm first ran a fuel cell for NASA, it also delivered its first commercial fuel cell to the Columbia Gulf Natural Gas Company. This modest 500-watt plant has been used by Columbia Gulf since then to power a control panel in one of its natural gas stations. Like the Apollo fuel cell, it runs on expensive oxygen and hydrogen rather than on natural gas. But by 1964 Pratt & Whitney was developing a commercial fuel cell generating a sizable 5 kilowatts, ten times the output of the pioneer Columbia Gulf installation, and operating not on hydrogen and oxygen, but on cheap methanol.

Men discovered the useful gas helium first in the sun. More recently we seem to be discovering the fuel cell in space vehicles. The space age, like nuclear energy, has resulted in some beneficial fallout; and among the best of this fallout seems to be the fuel cell.

CHAPTER EIGHT

Other Jobs for Fuel Cells

MILITARY and space applications represent a special and limited field for the fuel cell, and while military use of energy is fairly high, the civilian world represents a fantastic market. Of all the "commodities" bought and sold, energy ranks first. Not only does it heat and cool our homes, provide light and communication, get us where we want to go, but it is also used to produce and transport our food, clothes, and almost everything we buy. Here is the ultimate "down-to-earth" application of the fuel cell, as supplier of power for industry and for domestic uses.

The Domestic Fuel-cell Power Plant

Most homes have two utilities serving them from distant power plants: natural gas and electricity. There has been a trend toward all-electric power, and the advantages of such a system are obvious. There would be no need to run gas lines, with a resultant saving in capital costs. However, the natural-gas suppliers have another thought about this. They also suggest eliminating one of the utilities—that of electric power! Natural gas would be the fuel for a small fuel-cell

The experimental 5-kilowatt hydrocarbon-air fuel cell at left is compared with a standard generator of the same capacity.

power plant that would produce domestic electricity. Among the firms investigating this possibility is the Esso Research and Engineering Corporation, and Esso engineers foresee the cutting of utility bills in half.

In 1960, graduate students of Harvard Business School prepared a report entitled "Fuel Cells—Power for the Future." Included were statistics on the fuel cell as a power producer for domestic consumers. In one study, in which annual costs for conventional electricity were estimated at $126 for a small home using 3600 kilowatt-hours a year and requiring a power of three kilowatts, costs were estimated for various fuel-cell substitutes. It should be remembered that the fuel-cell system costs included the capital investment for the new power plant, while in the case of conventional electric power a central station already exists. We shall consider the significance of this factor later.

Using a hydrogen-oxygen fuel cell of the type available in 1960, the electricity would cost the home owner $783 per year. Compared with $126 for a public utility, this is hardly an attractive proposition, even after the cost of the fuel cell ($330) is written off.

Next to be considered was a "dissolved-fuel" fuel cell (of the methanol-air type which Esso successfully operated in 1965). This would cost the home owner $438 a year, and still does not represent an economical change in power supply.

Finally, the researchers investigated the costs of power supplied by a mass-produced low-temperature hydrocarbon fuel cell. The picture changes suddenly and drastically in favor of the fuel cell. First of all, the cost of the fuel cell itself would be only $36. Second, the annual cost for electricity would be just $44. This is about one-third the cost of conventional electricity and even in an area already served by a large central power station a homeowner could put in a home power plant and save two-thirds of his bill. He could buy a new fuel cell every year and still save almost half, but it is probable that a fuel cell will operate for many years with no maintenance problems or costs. There are many other potential advantages that we shall look at now.

Consider a new area of population, far removed from any source of electric power. Serving it with conventional power calls for expensive power lines, or erection of a large power plant locally at high cost. By installing individual fuel cells in basement or closet all this cost is saved.

In a city with no power poles or wires life would not only be more pleasant, it would be safe from the hazards of falling wires and youngsters climbing poles. Storms would not mean power failures, and in the case of bad weather or other emergency each home would be self-sufficient.

There are two ways in which the domestic fuel cell could be fueled. If natural gas is available, it could be piped to the home. If not, liquid fuel or bottled gas could power the plant.

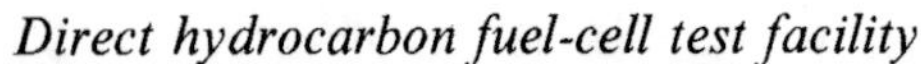
Direct hydrocarbon fuel-cell test facility

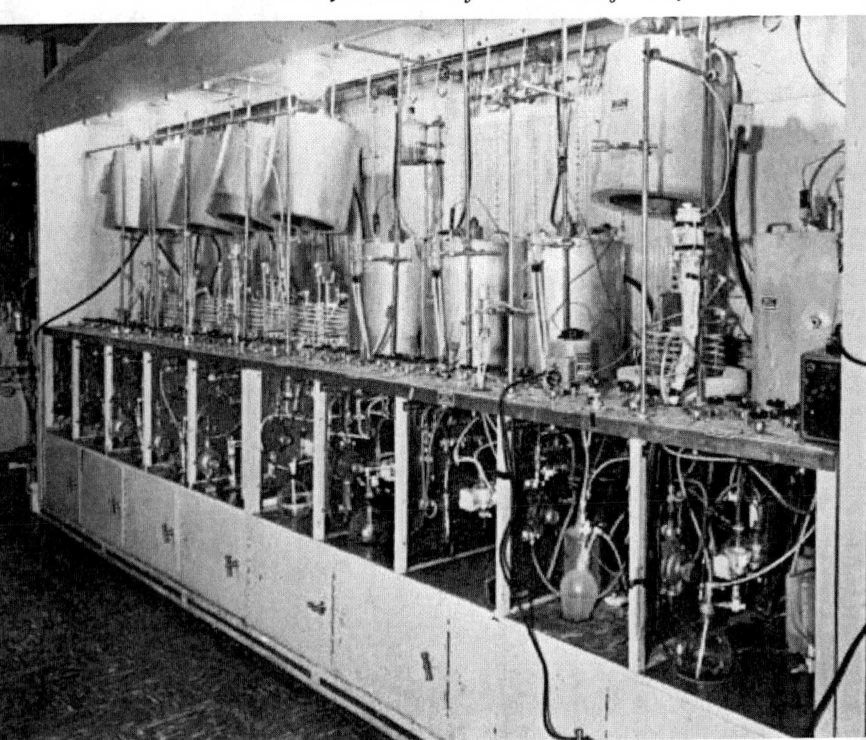

Many homeowners already use bottled gas or oil for heating; purchasing additional amounts for operation of the fuel cell would pose no problem. Even bringing home a five-gallon can of fuel occasionally would be no great inconvenience.

Some adjustment in the electrical system in the home would be required, of course, for switching to fuel cells. Most homes operate on 110 or 220 volts, so appliances are designed to use this supply. Where AC equipment is on hand, the fuel-cell plant would have to include conversion equipment from low-voltage DC to high-voltage AC, and this would add to the cost of the installation. In areas being newly developed, appliances designed for, say, 28 volts DC could be purchased.

Continuation of centralized power stations does not rule out the fuel cell, of course. With its high efficiency potential, it is a logical successor to the heat engine as new power plants are built. While the fuel cell does not now yield the high power density of a steam-electric plant, its 75 per cent efficiency is a strong factor in balancing out size and volume considerations. Maintenance costs should be lower, and the lifetime of a fuel cell will exceed that of a complicated piece of high-speed rotating equipment. Because the fuel cell produces no great amounts of waste heat, does not need large quantities of cooling water, and produces no noise—either acoustic or radio interference—it is a very desirable power supply. Perhaps the greatest advantage is that a fuel cell can be built as small as desired with little or no sacrifice in efficiency, a condition not true for the steam-electric or diesel plant.

The Fuel-cell Automobile

If there is a single piece of equipment that symbolizes modern man it is probably the automobile. Long ago, a political campaign was based on the slogan of "two cars in every garage." We have come to see that dream generally realized; we have also seen the dream turn into a nightmare. As someone has aptly put it, each one of us owns two cars and drives both of them at once. Some results of this civilization on wheels are of vital interest to us in this book about the fuel cell—for example, the fuel consumption of automobiles, and the matter of air pollution, more commonly called smog.

Living as we do in a sea of automobiles, it should come as no surprise to us that they consume an ocean of fuel. The amount of fuel required to keep us on the highways is second only to that used in heating homes. Quite obviously, anything that can be done to cut this use of petroleum will stretch out our supplies until we are able to develop substitute fuels at an economical price. The fuel cell, as we shall see, *can* cut our automotive fuel bills, particularly since it represents an efficiency potential several times greater than the gasoline engine which delivers only from 15 to 23 per cent.

Air pollution has rapidly become not merely a nuisance and destroyer of natural beauty, but a menace to health and safety. The automobile is not the only guilty contributor but it surely deserves a large share of the blame. Smog has killed thousands of people in England, killed them directly with its poisonous fumes. As yet there have been far fewer such outright deaths in the United States, but smog has caused accidents because of impaired visibility both for surface vehicles and aircraft. Smog doesn't just burn the eyes, it may be slowly poisoning us via the respiratory tract, and it is possible that deaths have been caused over a period of time by this air pollution.

One result of the smog menace is the institution of laws in some states requiring that smog-preventing devices be installed on automobiles. A longer-range plan calls for such installation at the factory as original equipment. Smog thus represents additional expense for the motorist, whether he is aware of it or not.

As yet we have not mentioned the dangers of carbon monoxide poisoning. Each year a large number of people end their lives, intentionally as suicides or accidentally as casualties of exhaust-gas poisoning. Leaky mufflers, operation of auto engines in the garage, and so on are responsible for such tragedies.

What is to be done about the smog problem? Perhaps the anti-smog mufflers will help. However, similar devices have been mandatory equipment for many factories, and these sources continue to clog the atmosphere with contaminants. Air pollution is not a minor inconvenience to fret about like humidity or mosquitoes. It is a serious problem that we are going to have to solve if we are not to face even more serious consequences than we dream might result.

One possible solution is the substitution of electricity for internal combustion in our automobiles, using fuel cells instead of gasoline or diesel engines. We are considering the electric automobile because of fuel economy and the elimination of harmful exhaust. There are many other advantages of a fuel-cell-operated car that are not so obvious:

Silence
Safety
Simplicity
Ease of maintenance
No lubrication required
No warm-up required

No fuel wasted at stop lights or other stops
Possibility of reclaiming energy during braking.

Internal-combustion engines are not the only power plants used in automobiles, of course. Steam engines have served, and many old-timers still sing the praises of the "Stanley Steamer." Even the electric car is no novelty, and has been built and used for many decades. Electric shopping carts, golf carts, and even large delivery trucks are on the job and doing excellent work. Operators of electric trucks point to service records of forty years and more with a piece of equipment, a record seldom attained by gasoline or diesel trucks, and then only with costly maintenance and periodic overhaul. But electric power carries with it some big drawbacks that have kept it from being widely used.

Until the fuel cell, all electric vehicles were battery-powered, or fed by rails or cable as in streetcars and trains. Both these systems leave something to be desired. The trolley car or electric train cannot leave its track. Battery-powered vehicles are heavy and limited in cruising range. So the internal-combustion engine has become favored for automobiles, and electric power plants have been relegated to a few minor tasks.

The fuel cell changes the picture dramatically. Even the expensive hydrogen-oxygen fuel cell compared not too badly with storage-battery golf carts and lift trucks. Allis-Chalmers' tractor of 20 horsepower proved that electric power was a lot closer than ever before. The acceptance of lightweight foreign cars in this country has helped to make the electric car more of a possibility in the near future. Since World War II these little cars have been imported by the millions to find real popularity in the United States, a land where horsepower

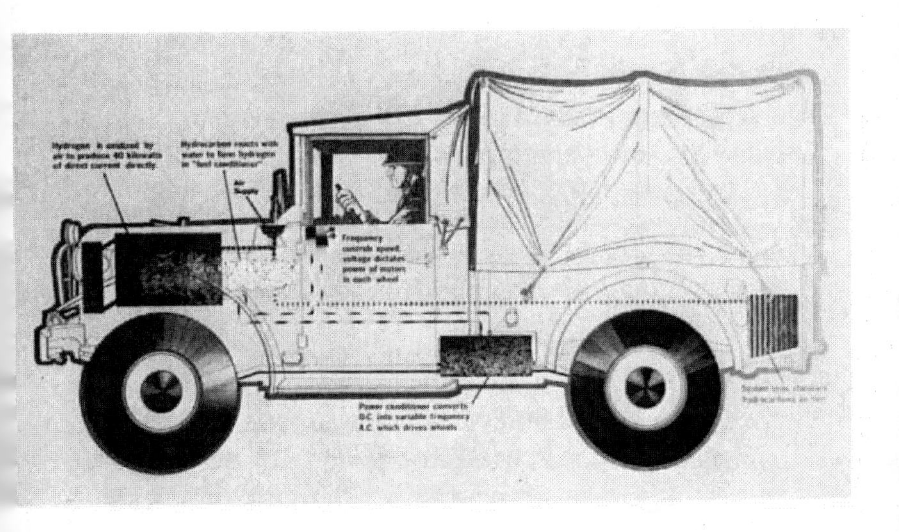

150 miles on a gallon of fuel is possible for this ¾-ton truck powered by a fuel cell.

is a status symbol. Here was a car with less than 50-horsepower being eagerly purchased by people who could have had 300-horsepower models just as easily.

The reason for the high horsepower ratings of American cars is related to such things as "rubber-burning ability" and snob appeal. In normal operation a big car uses only about one-fourth its power, but to deliver the expected acceleration the high horsepower rating is necessary. Many an owner of a 300-horsepower monster has been pulled out of the mud by a 20-horsepower tractor.

To move an automobile weighing 4,000 pounds at a speed of 85 miles an hour requires an engine of how much power? Surprisingly, 80 horsepower will do the job. Why are our cars equipped with 300-horsepower engines, then? Such overpowering is necessary to give us the acceleration we want at low speeds, during which we may use most of the available horsepower to produce the torque necessary. Torque is rotational force on a shaft or wheel. High torque at low speed requires an internal-combustion engine with high horsepower. For these reasons, the DC electric motor in some applications has better torque-speed characteristics.

While a gasoline engine must run at high speed to develop high torque, an electric motor delivers high torque even at low speeds. As an example, a manufacturer of delivery trucks makes two versions of his product; one fitted with a gasoline engine and the other an electric motor. The gasoline engine has a rating of 80 horsepower; the electric motor only 16 horsepower. This same ratio can be seen in lawnmowers, where the gasoline-engine rating for similar size mowers is several times that of electric motors.

Let us say we want to replace the 50-horsepower gasoline engine of our small foreign car with an electric motor capable of operating directly from a fuel cell. How large a motor will we need? Not 50 horsepower, or even 25 horsepower. For reasons we have discussed, about one-fourth of the 50 will deliver the same power. So a 12.5-horsepower DC electric motor will give us Volkswagen performance, and a fuel cell of that capacity will operate the motor.

Actually, we will install not one electric motor but four—one for each wheel. Each motor would be about 3 horsepower. This eliminates a lot of bothersome intermediate components like pistons, gears, shafts, and clutches. At the same time we have a sturdy four-wheel drive of the type we pay a premium for in conventional automobiles.

In our electric car we have fuel tank, fuel cell, wires to the individual motors and to the control panel, and the motors themselves. Notice that we eliminate a lot more than gears and drive shafts. In our new car we have no carburetor, distributor, spark plugs, points, coil, condenser, pistons, valves, muffler, exhaust pipe, starter, cooling system, timing mechanism, crankcase, gear shift, clutch, etc.

How about brakes? Conventional cars have hydraulic brakes composed of shoes, drums, tubing, and so on. This complicated system is so subject to failure that some manufacturers provide *two* complete hydraulic systems for safety. In the electric car we can use *electromagnetic* braking. Besides being a simple and trouble-free system, this offers another intriguing possibility. A certain percentage of the fuel we burn in our automobile is wasted in heat and noise as we brake for frequent stops, or going down steep hills. It is quite conceivable that this ordinarily wasted energy can be channeled back into our fuel cell as electricity as we operate the individual wheel motors in reverse. Normally they operate as motors and convert electricity into rotary motion. Used as brakes, they convert rotary motion into electricity which regenerates our fuel cell. Thus we boost even more the efficiency of our electric car, which is already far better than the internal-combustion engine it replaces.

Details have been worked out for a "second car" weighing 2400 pounds and having a top speed of 50 miles per hour. Using a hydrocarbon fuel cell and DC electric motors, the power plant would weigh 660 pounds, compared with from 400 to 600 for typical small gasoline engines. Its volume would be 13 cubic feet, compared with from 25 to 30 (and it would be easy to distribute the fuel-cell components throughout the car with a saving of space, and simplicity of design); cost of the power plant would be \$560 compared with \$400 to \$600.

Thus far the fuel-cell car seems to compare quite evenly with a gasoline-driven vehicle. Why bother to make the switch? Well, for one thing the operating costs would be considerably less. Researchers estimated from two to three cents per mile for the conventional car. The fuel-cell type would operate for less than half a cent a mile. At 10,000 miles a year this represents a saving of from \$150 to \$250. Add to this the bonus of clean, quiet, safe, trouble-free operation, and the over-all saving in precious petroleum, and the advantage of millions of fuel-cell electric cars should begin to be apparent.

For an eighty-mile-per-hour family car, the fuel-cell version would be handicapped by weighing some 1400 pounds more than a gasoline engine and costing about \$800 more for the power plant itself. It would, however, operate for about one-fifth the cost of the gasoline-driven car.

Similar comparisons have been worked out for trucks, tractors, locomotives, and marine engines. Assuming that a cheap hydrocarbon fuel cell is developed, it will operate more cheaply than conventional power plants in all these applications. Consider some of the advantages in a fuel-cell electric boat for fishing: easy starting, no burned fingers, no grease or oil, no ignition worries, plus silent operation. The same advantages apply to a fuel-cell lawnmower or auxiliary engine.

Only in the aviation field does there seem to be no advantage in using the new power plant. The reason is one of weight. A fuel cell plus a suitable electric motor for a light airplane would weigh about 1200 pounds *more* than the gasoline engine. Its fuel economy over the gas engine would make it competitive if the craft were to be flown for thirty hours or more, but this is not a practical consideration, as most flights in light planes are for only several hours.

Summary

Those who have studied the fuel cell as a new power source for vehicles foresee its success first in small equipment such as golf carts, lift trucks, light delivery vans, and so on. Once proved here, it will quite likely go on to be adopted for "second-car" use and eventually to supplant entirely the gasoline and diesel engine in ground and marine transportation. It is possible that "recharging" may be done overnight in the garage, rather than by refueling. In other words, the regenerative fuel cell would be used, with electricity pumped in reverse through the electrodes to recharge the working fluid in the tank. For twenty-four-hour availability, vehicles could also be fueled at filling stations just like a gasoline engine, and the by-product drained off as waste. A waste, however, that would not pollute the atmosphere. Either way, the fuel cell should nearly double our fuel supply—by conserving it.

CHAPTER NINE

How To Make a Demonstration Fuel Cell*

WHILE RESEARCH LABORATORIES are developing fuel-cell designs costing thousands of dollars in their initial stages, a simple fuel cell capable of producing 6 to 10 milliamperes of current at 0.5 volt (ample power for a transistor radio also described) can be constructed for about ten dollars.

Almost any chemical operation can be made dangerous through carelessness. However, a fuel cell can be built with complete safety by taking sensible precautions.

Read the instructions carefully before starting to work and think about each step before doing it. Keep in mind the following points:

SAFETY RULES FOR BUILDING A FUEL CELL

1. All of the chemicals—potassium hydroxide, methyl alcohol, silver nitrate and chloroplatinic acid—are poisonous.
2. The vapors of methyl alcohol are toxic and flammable.
3. Silver nitrate and potassium hydroxide are corrosive and cause severe burns upon contact with eyes or skin. Potassium hydroxide in solution will attack skin, clothing, painted surfaces and aluminum much as a very strong household lye.

* Courtesy of Esso Research and Engineering Co.

4. Take every precaution to avoid accidental contact with the chemicals. Specific instructions for treating accidental contacts are given for each chemical in the section that covers the chemical's use.

5. Wear safety glasses when working with any of the chemicals. Put them on before opening the chemical containers and keep them on while building and working with the cell itself.

This chapter describes the operating principles of a simple, unpressurized cell which works at room temperature, using methyl alcohol as a fuel and oxygen from the air as an oxidant. It explains how to build and operate this cell and shows how to construct a transistor radio which can be operated from the fuel cell. The radio components cost about eight dollars.

PRINCIPLES OF OPERATION

Basically the cell consists of a fuel electrode and an oxygen electrode. Both are immersed in an electrolyte which is a solution of potassium hydroxide in water. The fuel, methyl alcohol, is mixed with the potassium hydroxide solution. Air is bubbled over the oxygen electrode. The following equations show the reactions:

AT THE OXYGEN ELECTRODE

$$O_2 \text{ (gas)} + 2\,H_2O + 4 \text{ Electrons} \longrightarrow 4OH^-$$

from the air	electrode needs 4 electrons	hydroxyl ions

AT THE FUEL ELECTRODE

$$CH_3OH + 4\ OH^- \longrightarrow HCOOH + 3H_2O + 4\ \text{Electrons}$$

methyl alcohol	formic acid	electrode has 4 extra electrons

OVER-ALL REACTION $O_2 + CH_3OH \longrightarrow HCOOH + H_2O$

adding above two	+ a net flow of 4 electrons from the fuel electrode to the oxygen electrode through the external circuit connecting the two electrodes.

In this operation, oxygen gas from the air bubbles is adsorbed onto the oxygen electrode. Oxygen then reacts at the electrode with the water in the electrolyte solution ($KOH + H_2O$) to produce negatively charged hydroxyl ions (OH^-). The creation of these negatively charged ions leaves the oxygen electrode with a *deficiency* of electrons (a need for electrons, e^-). The OH^- ions migrate through the electrolyte solution to the fuel electrode where they react with methyl alcohol, which has been adsorbed from the solution onto this electrode. The reaction produces formic acid (HCOOH), water and electrons. Thus there is an *excess* of electrons on the fuel electrode. If the two electrodes are connected by an external electrical circuit, four electrons will flow from the fuel electrode (which has an excess) to the oxygen electrode (which has a deficiency) for each molecule of methyl alcohol which reacts. This flow of electrons is a current which can power a radio or do other useful work. Although the equations and sketch show the production of formic acid (HCOOH), this organic acid immediately reacts with the KOH to produce the water-soluble potassium salt of this acid, HCOOK.

Electrodes Are Coated With Catalysts

The fuel and oxygen electrodes used to make the cell described in this chapter are made of nickel screen. In order to make the reaction at each electrode go at a rate fast enough to produce a measurable current (electron flow), *catalysts* are placed upon each electrode. The catalyst used on the methyl alcohol fuel electrode is *platinum black* (a finely divided form of metallic platinum). It is put on the screen by soaking the nickel screen in a water solution of chloroplatinic acid ($PtCl_4 \cdot 2HCl \cdot nH_2O$). The platinum ions in the water solution deposit on the nickel in the form of platinum metal (platinum black), and some of the nickel goes into the solution as nickel ions. The oxygen electrode is catalyzed with silver. The nickel screen is soaked in a water solution of silver nitrate ($AgNO_3$). Metallic silver is deposited on the nickel screen and some of the nickel goes into the solution. Without these catalysts, the reaction would proceed too slowly to produce a usable amount of power.

MATERIALS AND INGREDIENTS NEEDED TO BUILD THE FUEL CELL

nickel screen, grade A, 150-mesh, 5 x 12-inch sheet
1 gram chloroplatinic acid
5 grams silver nitrate
100 grams potassium hydroxide
35 milliliters methyl alcohol
600 milliliter Pyrex beaker

10 feet of bell wire
3 x 5-inch sheet of blotting or filter paper
2 alligator clips
3 feet of plastic or rubber tubing
safety glasses

COMPONENTS FOR MEASURING CELL PERFORMANCE

100-ohm resistor
DC voltmeter (Reading in 0–1 volt range)
DC milliammeter (Reading in 0–10 milliamp. range)
If available, a 0–10,000-ohm variable resistance.

MATERIALS FOR RADIO

2 transistors, Ck 722 Raytheon
1 diode IN 34A, Sylvania
1 midget TRF tuning capacitor (1 section, 15–400 MMFD)
1 antenna coil, type 70A (540–1600KC)
2 25-MFD capacitors
1 0.01-MFD capacitor
1 3300-ohm resistor, type GBT, ½-watt
2 0.27-megohm resistors, type GBT, ½-watt
1 single headphone
1 25-foot spool plastic hookup wire
20 1½-inch twin Fahnestock clips
(Where-to-purchase information can be found at end of chapter.)

PREPARATION OF ELECTRODES

The first step is to coat the nickel screen electrodes with catalysts. Cut two 2 x 5-inch strips of nickel screen. Remove all traces of grease or oil by washing them in a dry-cleaning solvent or lighter fluid.

Fuel Electrode

To deposit platinum-black catalyst on the methyl alcohol fuel electrode, dissolve 1 gram of chloroplatinic acid ($PtCl_4 \cdot 2HCl \cdot nH_2O$) in 100 milliliters (3.4 fluid ounces) of water. Use distilled water if available. Soak one of the 2 x 5-inch nickel screen strips in this solution for about one hour. Turn the screen over several times to get an even coating of platinum. Rinse the screen thoroughly with water and store in water until used. *Never allow it to dry out.* (The chloroplatinic acid solution can be saved and used again.)

Treatment for accidental contact: Wash thoroughly with water. This applies to contact with either the chloroplatinic acid powder or the solution.

Oxygen Electrode

To deposit the silver catalyst on the oxygen electrode, dissolve 5 grams of silver nitrate ($AgNO_3$) in 100 milliliters of water—preferably distilled water. Soak the remaining 2 x 5-inch nickel screen in this solution for about one hour. Turn the screen over several times to get an even coating. Rinse thoroughly and store in water until used. (The solution can be saved and used again.)

Treatment for accidental contact: Immediately wash with large quantities of water. This applies to contact with either the crystals or the solution of silver nitrate.

PREPARATION OF POTASSIUM HYDROXIDE SOLUTION

The 600-milliliter Pyrex beaker in which the potassium hydroxide solution will be prepared should be placed—and kept—in a flat-bottomed container made of iron, glass or pottery. This guards against the beaker's being tipped over accidentally and will contain any solution that may spill or splash.

Into the beaker put 300 milliliters (about 10 fluid ounces) of water. Use distilled water if available. Very slowly add 100 grams (3.5 ounces) of potassium hydroxide (KOH). The solution will become fairly hot. Allow it to cool before using.

Treatment for accidental contact: Immediately wash the exposed area thoroughly with water, flushing for at least fifteen minutes. Follow the water wash with a lemon juice or vinegar wash if it is available, then by more water. If contact with the skin is extensive, or if the eyes are involved, see a physician after washing as described above.

ASSEMBLY OF FUEL CELL

The fuel cell will be assembled in the beaker of potassium hydroxide solution—still held in the larger container.

Put the two electrodes in the beaker of solution, placing them on opposite sides of the beaker. Bend the upper edges of the screens over the lip of the beaker to hold them in place. Insert a blotter or folded filter paper between the screens to prevent their touching each other and short-circuiting the cell. However, the screens may touch the paper without short-circuiting the cell. Add 35 milliliters (slightly over 1 fluid ounce) of methyl alcohol. Place one end of the plastic or rubber tubing between the silver-coated oxygen electrode and the side of the beaker.

The cell is now ready to operate. As soon as an electrical connection is made between the two electrodes, methyl alcohol will react at the fuel electrode (anode) and oxygen from the air will react at the oxygen electrode (cathode). The oxygen reaction occurs mainly at the interface where air and solution meet on the silver-coated screen.

OPERATION OF THE FUEL CELL

Attach the alligator clips to the electrode screens and, using the bell wire, connect the voltmeter and milliammeter as shown on this page. With the milliammeter circuit open, as shown on this page, you can measure the open circuit (or "no load") voltage of the cell since very little current flows through the high resistance of the voltmeter. When the milliammeter circuit is closed, current will flow through the low resistance of the milliammeter and the cell voltage will fall to almost zero. This drop in voltage is due mainly to polarization or energy loss at the electrodes. The over-all reaction at each electrode takes place in a complicated series of steps.

In some of these steps, energy that one would like to get in the form of electricity is released instead as heat. The amount of polarization depends on the rate at which the reaction is taking place—that is to say, on the amount of current being produced by the cell.

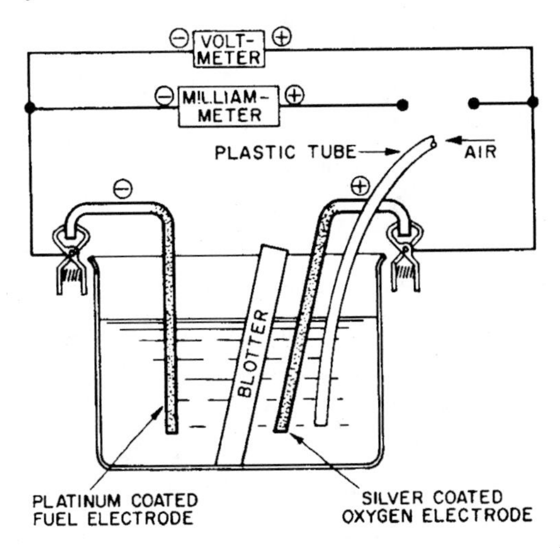

Assembled fuel cell with "no load" circuit

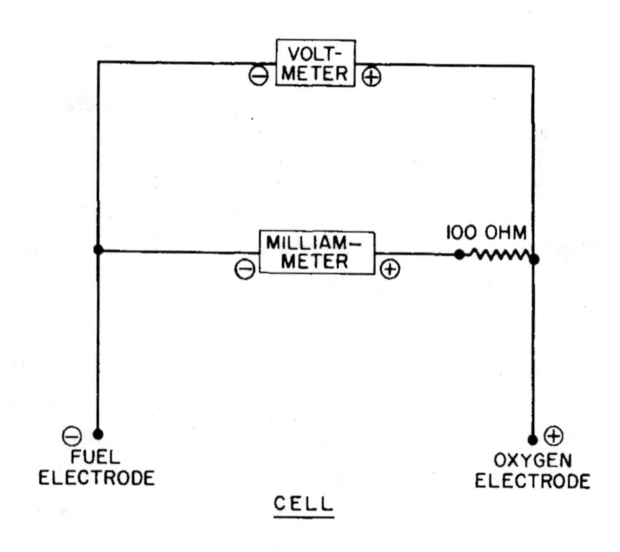

Load circuit

To demonstrate this, connect the 100-ohm resistor in series with the milliammeter as shown on this page. With this higher resistance, less current is drawn from the cell than with the milliammeter alone in the circuit, and polarization decreases.

The cell voltage will now drop to 0.1 or 0.2 volts instead of almost to zero. A large part of the voltage loss is occurring at the oxygen electrode where most of the reaction is taking place at the rather small liquid-air interface region. The rate of reaction on this small area is high and polarization is high.

By blowing *gently* into the plastic tube (or using a controlled flow of compressed air) you can feed oxygen to the oxygen electrode and increase the useful current-producing area (which is the electrode area in intimate contact with air and solution). As you do this the voltage will rise.

CAUTION: Do not blow hard; bubble the air *gently* over the electrode to prevent spraying the corrosive KOH solution. Be particularly careful not to suck any of the solution into your mouth.

If a 0–10,000-ohm variable resistance is available, it can be wired into the circuit in place of the 100-ohm resistor and the relationship between current flow and voltage (controlled by amount of resistance) can be determined. With air bubbling, the cell output will approach 0.01 watt. With pure oxygen, the output would be several times larger. However, even without air bubbling, the cell will produce enough power to operate a transistorized radio receiver like the one shown in the schematic drawing on page 140.

ASSEMBLY OF A TRANSISTOR RADIO POWERED BY FUEL CELL

The radio may be wired "breadboard" fashion on a 7 x 12-inch piece of board as shown in the photo. Any type of wire may be used in place of the hookup wire suggested in the parts list in this chapter. The Fahnestock clips are convenient and avoid the need for soldering. However, finishing nails can be driven into the board and used as soldered connecting posts in place of the clips.

Transistors

As shown on page 140, there are 3 leads: the Emitter "E," the Base "B," and the Collector "C," occurring in that order. There is a red dot next to the Collector "C." Protect the transistors from heat during soldering by placing a knife blade on the transistor lead between the transistor and the connection being soldered.

25 MFD Capacitors

Note the + and – markings shown on page 140. These same markings are on the capacitor. Connect the capacitor as shown in the figure. The 0.01-MFD capacitor has no markings and can be connected in either direction.

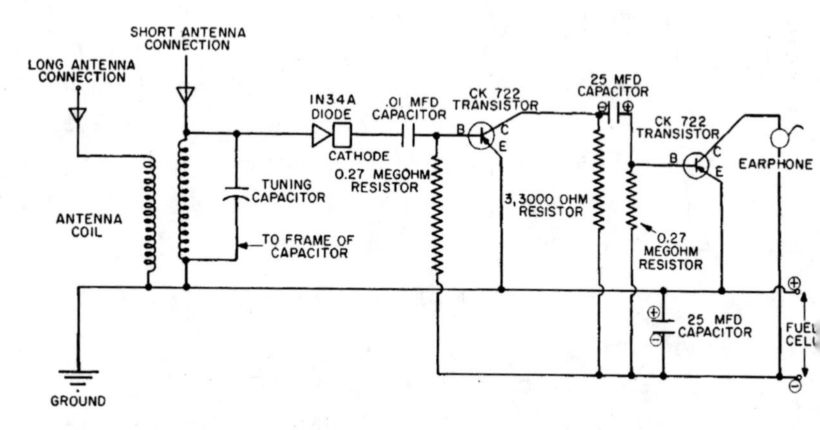

Schematic diagram of transistor radio receiver

Resistors

The two 0.27-megohm resistors and the 3300-ohm resistor can be identified by the Color Code bands on the resistors.

0.27-megohm	3300-ohm
Red	Orange
Violet	Orange
Yellow	Red
Silver	Silver

Diode

Note the location of the cathode. Colored bands are located on the cathode end of the diode.

Tuning Capacitor

Note that one connection is made to the metal frame of the capacitor; the other connection is made to any one of the several terminals on the capacitor.

Antenna Coil

Make sure the antenna coil is grounded as shown in the figure. If the leads are not marked to show which is the "long" antenna coil and which is the "short," connect one end of

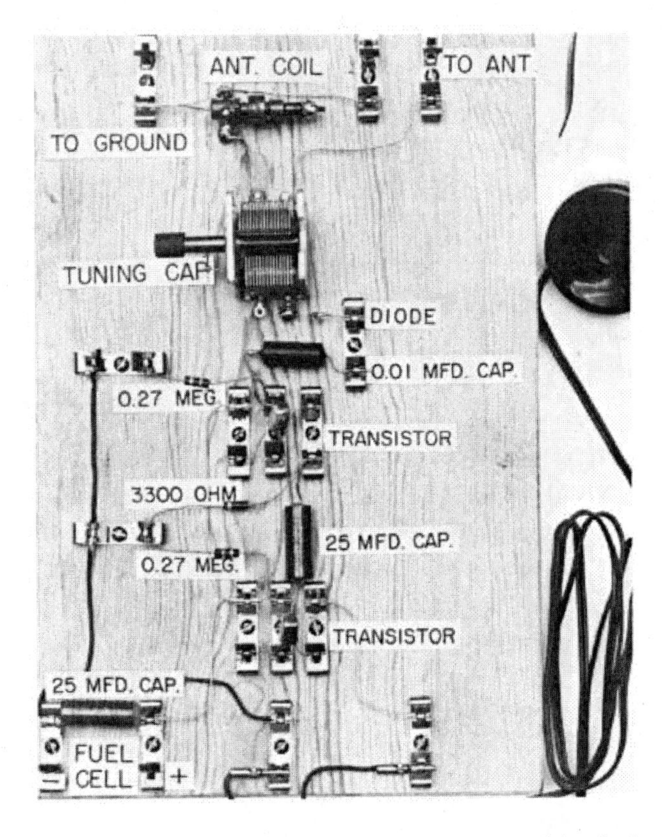

"Breadboard" wiring of transistor radio powered by fuel cell

each coil (these will be color-coded or numbered on the manufacturer's instruction sheet) to ground as shown in the figure. Then connect the antenna to each coil in turn to see which connection gives a stronger signal. Make sure the antenna itself is *not* grounded. Use a long antenna wire in weak radio signal areas and a shorter antenna in strong signal areas. In a steel framed building it is necessary to place the antenna outside the building.

When connecting the fuel cell to the radio, make sure the negative platinum black fuel electrode is connected to the negative (refer to page 140) radio input terminal or the radio will not operate. At the low power level required by the radio (about 100 microwatts) it is possible to operate the radio continuously for several months with the fuel cell. It is not necessary to bubble air to the silver-coated oxygen electrode since sufficient oxygen will adsorb to produce the small power requirement. If the cell is to be used over a period of time, a piece of waxed paper on top of the cell will aid in preventing the methyl alcohol from vaporizing.

WHERE TO OBTAIN MATERIALS FOR FUEL CELL

The materials and chemicals needed to build the fuel cell can be obtained from many scientific or drug supply houses. The names of suppliers have been listed below only as a guide for obtaining the harder-to-find items.

nickel screen, grade A, 150-mesh — Minimum order: $1.65 including postage for 5 x 12-inch sheet

Newark Wire Cloth Co.
351 Verona Avenue
Newark 4, New Jersey

1 gm. chloroplatinic acid — 1 gm., $4.75 including postage

Ace Scientific Supply Co.
1420 East Linden Avenue
Linden, New Jersey

5 gm. silver nitrate	Minimum order: 1 oz., $2.56 including postage
Ace Scientific Supply Co.	
100 gm. potassium hydroxide	Minimum order: 1 lb. Technical Grade Flakes, $0.85
Ace Scientific Supply Co.	*(Shipped express collect only)
35 ml. methyl alcohol	Minimum order: 1 pt. Reagent Grade, $0.92
Ace Scientific Supply Co.	*(Shipped express collect only)

* Because shipping costs are high and, depending on the distance, may be much more than the actual cost of the item, we strongly suggest purchasing locally if at all possible.

MATERIALS FOR RADIO

The radio components may be obtained at any electronic-supply house. The stock numbers of Allied Radio, 100 N. Western Avenue, Chicago 80, Illinois, are given for convenience.

	Allied Stock No.
2 transistors, CK 722 Raytheon	5E 822
1 dioide IN 34A, Sylvania	9E 750
1 midget TRF tuning capacitor (1 section, 15–400 MMFD)	61H009
1 antenna coil, type 70A (540–1600KC)	60H866
2 25-MFD capacitors	13L842
1 0.01-MFD capacitor	19L010
1 3300-ohm resistor, type GBT, ½-watt	1MM000
2 0.27-megohm resistors, type GBT, ½-watt	1MM000
1 single headphone	59J112
1 25-foot spool plastic hookup wire	47TT214
20 1½-inch twin Fahnestock clips	41H715

CHAPTER TEN

The Fuel Cell Tomorrow

IT WOULD not be correct to say that the fuel cell has "arrived" as the new power source for the world. Despite the successes of the device in space applications and a few tests with more conventional tasks, the fuel cell is still a minor factor in the production of electric power. In this chapter we shall consider it not merely for special applications such as Gemini and Apollo, submarines, and certain military field generators, but as a supplier of power on a broad scale.

While its future looks very bright, there are some authorities who feel that the fuel cell has been overglamorized. For example, a spokesman for a large oil firm said in 1965 that his organization does not expect fuel cells to make an impression on our energy picture of the future. While fuel cells may compete with dry-cell batteries for a few special purposes, he stated, the present high interest in the fuel cell would be likely to die off soon unless there is a development of some significant commercial applications.

While this is certainly a possibility that must be considered even by the most enthusiastic proponents of the fuel cell, the view that there will be no significant commercial uses for the device is not widespread. In addition to the fifty million dollars spent on developing fuel cells for our space programs, about that same amount is spent each year by private firms in research and development of fuel cells for all purposes. In the United States, for example, dozens of organizations have active programs involving fuel cells. An indication of the interest of the conventional utility producers is the work of the Institute of Gas Technology in Chicago, Illinois. The program here is concerned with the use of natural gas as a fuel. The goal is to produce as much as 30 kilowatt-hours of electricity from one "therm" of natural gas, costing about ten cents.

England was most responsible for the fuel cell in the first place, and the work is continuing there. Among the British organizations active are the Sondes Place Research Institute, Dorking, Surrey, where the high-temperature fuel cell is of particular interest. The French Institute of Petroleum in Paris is pursuing studies of the fuel cell, both as a source of electric power and as an electrochemical producer of useful products. In little Switzerland, the firm of Brown, Boveri and Company is in the forefront of fuel-cell research and development. Russia has for many years been active in the fuel cell field. At the Institute of Technical Physics in Braunschweig, Germany, Professor E. Justi and his co-workers continue their work that has already led to the much improved "double-skeleton" electrodes mentioned in Chapter 3. Work on the fuel cell at the Central Technical Institute at The Hague, The Netherlands, has been going on since 1950, and the men involved include such authorities as G. H. J. Broers and J. A. A. Ketelaar.

This high-level interest must arise from sound reasons.

Basically, these reasons stem from a single factor: the ever increasing use by human beings of energy to produce power. Man was once content with—or at least limited to—only one *man*power in the conduct of his daily living routine. Today this power picture has changed to an extent we do not appreciate because most of us have not known what it was like to be without all the power we demand now. However, in round numbers each one of us now uses the equivalent of about 40 *horse*power in the various machines at our disposal. If we assume that one horsepower is the equivalent of about six manpower, then each of us has something like 250 "energy slaves" working for us.

This is a far better state of affairs than having to do all the labor ourselves, but it leads to some problems. The United States uses up more than one-third of all the fuel consumed in the world, even though our population is only 6 per cent of the total. The trend of less-developed nations is toward copying our lead in energy consumption, and global population is exploding rapidly. The net result of all this is the prediction that in the next thirty-five years, man will burn up *three times as much* fossil fuel as he has burned in all previous history!

In spite of this tremendous use of fuel, we are not going to run out of coal and oil and natural gas in thirty-five years, of course. Fortunately, there seem to be trillions of tons of coal as yet unmined (although it becomes more expensive to mine as it gets scarcer) and billions of barrels of oil yet untapped (but in the United States we are forced to import increasing amounts of liquid fuels each year). When the oil is gone there is still lots of shale, although recovery of this low-grade fuel will increase the cost of power when it is necessary to go to this extreme.

There is little agreement on just how much more fuel we do have available. Estimates range from a fifty- to a twenty-five-hundred-year supply, with the latter based on discovery of vast reserves not yet known. There is agreement that *some* definite limit to our fossil fuels exists, however. Unfortunately, there is a tendency to shrug our shoulders and say that it makes little difference anyhow, now that we have nuclear energy: the "peaceful atom bomb" will soon be producing more than enough electricity, and at ridiculously low prices. Let's see how factual this picture really is.

As soon as the use of nuclear energy for production of power was shown to be possible, great hopes and marvelous predictions were made. If the energy in a teaspoon of nuclear fuel could drive a ship across the sea, surely the tons and tons of uranium in the world would make obsolete all our fears of fuel shortage. But today there are sobering warnings that nuclear energy is not so wonderful as all that. Only uranium 235 among the natural materials is usable "as is" for fuel in nuclear reactors, and the Atomic Energy Commission estimates that our total domestic reserves of U-235 would provide energy for only about twenty years in the United States!

By 1965 the United States had spent about thirty-four billion dollars in development of nuclear energy as a weapon and as a power source. Only about 1,000 megawatts of commercial nuclear electricity was being produced—of a total of 220,000 megawatts—but plans are for nuclear plants to generate half the electric power for the country by the year 2000. A little thought will show that all the U-235 would about be used up by then and nuclear energy might well be the most expensive power source ever resorted to. Happily there is something called the "breeder reactor" in which uranium is converted to power—plus more fuel than it burns.

In this manner it is possible to use more plentiful uranium-238 and thorium-232 in addition to just uranium-235. This would increase the energy available to nuclear reactors by about 100 times and provide fuel for two thousand years rather than just twenty. Again, it seems that science has provided an easy out for us. But the breeder reactor is not yet demonstrated as practical and one expert has predicted that it will take several—or even many—more years.

Much further in the future is the fusion process for producing power. This fantastic harnessing of the energy in "heavy water" by converting it to helium holds out the tantalizing prospect of adequate energy for thousands of years to come. But usable energy from fusion, despite accelerated programs for its development for some fifteen years, is still admittedly far from being realized, if indeed it ever will be.

Even supposing development of practical breeder reactors at an early date, there remain some very real problems for the nuclear power plant. One is the hazard of accidental release of radioactive material. Plants must be built at prescribed distances from populated areas to guard against such a catastrophe, and even with this safety factor there are some areas that have not accepted the nuclear plant. In the event of war, nuclear power plants would be prime targets for a double reason: the disruption of domestic and industrial life by cutting off power, and also the spreading of radioactive contamination about the target area. Another problem is the disposal of waste material. Present methods of encasing it in lead containers and sinking it in the ocean suggest the threat of pollution of the oceans, on which we are increasingly dependent.

Nuclear energy, then, for all its wonderful promise poses

some tremendous problems. For a long time in the future, fossil fuels like coal, oil, and natural gas must provide the bulk of the world's power supply. Even forgetting the conscientious concern we should feel for posterity, the shortage of fuel will be felt in rising prices for power. This by itself should prove to be a powerful incentive for the development of a power plant that is more efficient than conventional present-day utilities.

The fact that fossil fuels will provide us with most of our power for some years to come is another powerful argument for the development of the fuel cell. In noting the contamination danger posed by a nuclear power plant we should not assume that conventional fuel-burning power plants are blameless in this respect. In fact, the combustion of fossil fuels in the production of power represents a potentially greater, and certainly more immediate, danger than the depletion of our energy supplies.

In the production of more and more power for our modern civilization we are exploiting not just fuel but also the oxidant necessary to support the combustion of fossil fuels. Combustion is the combination of fuel and air, with the resultant release of heat energy and waste gases. As these wastes mix with our atmosphere, the air is slowly contaminated with a variety of chemicals from carbon dioxide to sulfuric compounds. The result is smog, or haze, or smoke. By whatever name, the result is the same: we are poisoning the air we breathe, and long before we run out of fuel we may have run out of safely breathable air.

Cavemen had the disadvantage of only one manpower, but the healthful benefits of fresh air. Today we have plenty of power but an increasingly contaminated atmosphere. Tragically, the smog that smudges the sky is far more than a nuisance that hampers our vision and burns our eyes. In mid-1965 residents of New York City were told that in a single month many tons of "dust" fall on the nation's largest city. Although this fallout is not radioactive, it contains such harmful chemicals as sulfur dioxide and benzpyrene. The latter is present in sufficient quantity to make breathing New York air equivalent to smoking two packs of cigarettes daily. Air pollution is considered a factor in the rising rate of deaths from cancer, and also in such epidemic diseases as Asian flu.

Besides the rather obvious fact that we are poisoning ourselves with smog are the added tragedies of the destruction of plant life in such areas, and the hazard that smog represents to airplanes and ground travel as well. It is the boast of power producers that a kilowatt-hour of electricity costs only about half a cent, but we are paying a far greater price in health as power plants, factories, and automobiles belch torrents of smoke into an increasingly deadly atmosphere.

The smog problem is nothing new. England, with its heavy use of coal, has long been a sufferer. From New York on the eastern coast to Los Angeles across the continent, the United States is plagued with smog. Laws have been passed insisting on the use of equipment to precipitate harmful chemicals before they leave chimneys, trash burning is prohibited, and anti-smog devices are being demanded for automobiles. The smog, however, is increasing. Even cities long noted for their clear air, such as Phoenix, Arizona, are worriedly counting the contaminants per million parts of air and watching visibility slowly decrease.

There is a longer range possibility that has been voiced by a number of scientists not given to scaremongering. This is the addition of so much carbon dioxide to our atmosphere that we seriously affect environmental conditions on our planet. The per cent of increase of this material is known, although we are not sure about the others. While carbon dioxide in itself is not a poison, it has the effect of trapping more heat in the atmosphere. In time this could raise the earth's temperature high enough to melt ice caps and thus flood civilized areas. Playing with fire can be a dangerous business, man is belatedly finding out.

Great weather-modifying schemes have been proposed to eliminate temperature inversions that are contributing factors to the smog condition. Even if successful, such grandiose plans would consume as much fuel as is presently being expended for *every* use, thus doubling not only the pollution problem but also the problem of dwindling resources.

Which brings us back to the fuel cell. By its nature it is not a producer of harmful exhaust as are conventional combustion engines. What by-product is produced is far more easy to recover and even to use profitably. A fuel cell is safe to use aboard a closed spaceship or submarine, while an internal combustion engine is not. Each of these applications represents a "closed-ecology" cycle. The earth is a "closed ecology" too, on a tremendously larger scale and the fuel cell offers the same advantages in this total environment.

Here are two powerful arguments then, for more widespread commercial use of the fuel cell: (1) It would save fuel, and (2) it surely would lessen the contamination of the air we breathe. Either or both of these advantages should be sufficient, although it seems probable that if we don't make use of the second, the first will be meaningless.

Time tables for the future are tricky things, but we might

hazard a few predictions as to where and when the fuel cell will continue to make itself felt in the world of power. Space flight offered the first practical applications. Next, in the submarine, and for a number of other military purposes the fuel cell should be used on a fairly broad scale. Electrochemical industries, such as the aluminum producers who need electricity in direct-current form, may be the first non-military users of fuel cells in volume.

A small generator, such as is used for an Army radar set in the field, might also serve domestically in remote areas to provide power for weather stations, airway beacons, and so on. As an auxiliary electric power source, for example as standby in hospitals, communications equipment, and so on, the fuel cell may make its first inroads against the conventional central power station.

Somewhere along the line it appears inevitable that automobiles, and maybe even larger vehicles, will switch to electric power in an effort to clear the air so that drivers and passengers will be able to live to drive. When this happens, the fuel cell is a hands-down favorite for the job.

Last of all, it seems, will be the substitution of fuel-cell plants for steam- or gas-turbine electric or nuclear-electric plants. Perhaps the fuel cell will be paired with a nuclear reactor in the regenerative configuration we discussed in an earlier chapter.

With no noisy fanfare such as attended the coming of the nuclear age, the fuel-cell age is on us. Far less spectacular, the modest "battery with a gas tank" nevertheless promises much for civilization in its quest for more and more power.

Glossary

Anode The positive terminal of a cell or battery

Aqueous electrolyte A liquid solution used in low-temperature fuel cells

Bacon cell An intermediate temperature and pressure hydrogen-oxygen fuel cell developed by Francis Bacon

Biochemical fuel cell A fuel cell in which the reaction is carried out by living organisms

Carbox fuel cell A carbon-oxygen fuel cell

Carnot principle The principle that states the efficiency of a heat engine depends on the absolute temperature difference between intake and exhaust of the engine

Catalyst Material or substance which aids in the carrying out of a desired reaction

Cathode The negative terminal of a cell or battery

Cryogenic Condition of very low temperature

Direct-reaction fuel cell Fuel cell in which no intermediate steps are required in converting fuel to energy; uses porous electrodes and one electrolyte

Dissolved-fuel fuel cell Fuel cell in which the fuel is added directly to the electrolyte

Drowning Drawing of water into the pores of an electrode, with resultant stoppage of fuel-cell reaction

Electrode A device which makes electrical contact with the electrolyte and serves as a terminal for attachment of an external circuit

Electrolyte A non-metallic conductor of electricity in which current is carried by the movement of ions

Electromotive force Any force that tends to produce a flow of electricity

Electron transport The movement of electrons from one electrode of fuel cell to the other

Endothermic reaction Reaction in which less energy is produced than was required to start the reaction

Exothermic reaction Reaction in which more energy is released than was required to start reaction

Flooding of electrodes Drawing of electrolyte into pores of electrodes, with resultant stopping of fuel-cell reaction

Fossil fuels Coal, oil, and natural gas; created by nature from fossilized life forms

Galvanic action Production of electricity by dissimilar materials

Hydrocarbon Substances made up of molecules containing atoms of hydrogen and carbon

Hydrox fuel cell Fuel cell using hydrogen and oxygen as reactants

Intermediate-reaction fuel cell Fuel cell in which non-porous electrodes are used and each electrode immersed in a separate electrolyte. Reaction products are removed externally.

Ion A free electron, or atom or molecule with an electrical charge

Ion-exchange membrane A solid electrolyte, usually a plastic film, that permits the passage of desired ions

Molten-salt electrolyte High-temperature electrolyte, usually a mixture of chlorides, carbonates, and hydrides

Oxidant Substance which causes combination of an element or compound with oxygen

Oxidation Reaction of an element or compound with oxygen. In this process the atoms of the oxidized material lose electrons.

Reactant The fuel or oxidant used in fuel cells

Redox fuel cell Fuel cell which makes use of the reduction-oxidation process to transfer electrons from one substance to another

Reformer Equipment for converting a cheap hydrocarbon fuel into a form more easily used in the fuel cell

Regenerative fuel cell Fuel cell in which the same medium, liquid metal, for example, is used over and over, with energy added to that medium externally and usually in the form of heat

Stack A number of individual fuel cells joined together to provide the required voltage and current

Wetting Filling of electrode pores with excess water produced in the fuel-cell reaction and not carried off as it should be (sometimes called "drowning")

Index